Concept Cartoons™

In Mathematics Education

Brenda Keogh

John Dabell

Stuart Naylor

Millgate House Education

First published in 2008 by Millgate House Publishers

Millgate House Publishers is an imprint of

Millgate House Education Ltd

Millgate House

30 Mill Hill Lane

Sandbach

Cheshire, CW11 4PN, UK

www.millgatehouse.co.uk

British Library Cataloguing in Publication Data

A catalogue record for this book is available from the British Library.

ISBN   978-0-59556260-1-2
EAN   9780955626012

Graphic Design by Lauren Barnes
Illustrations by Ged Mitchell

Printed and bound in Great Britain by
Crewe Colour Printers

Contents

i. Acknowledgements

This book (and CD ROM) follows its partner publication, Concept Cartoons in Science Education (Naylor and Keogh, 2000). We have used a broadly similar format for the Concept Cartoons and the background text, so that readers who are familiar with the science Concept Cartoons will feel at home with these examples in mathematics.

Our thanks go to:

- Illustrator (and landscape artist) Ged Mitchell, whose drawings bring our books alive

- Graphic designer and project manager Lauren Barnes, whose questions, comments and ideas have added sparkle to the book and CD ROM

- Software developer David Osborn at Angel Solutions, whose special skills have made the Concept Cartoons more interactive than we thought would be possible

- Colleagues, teachers and learners of all ages, who have provided the inspiration for many of the Concept Cartoons

- Teachers and advisers in North Yorkshire, Cheshire, Cornwall and Edinburgh, especially John Crosland and Peter Gorrie, who have provided invaluable help in developing and trialling the Concept Cartoons

- Costel Harnasz, Melvyn Cole and Gordon Stainsby, who helped with the editing process, and have added great insight to the Concept Cartoons

- John Dabell, whose imaginative ideas have helped to create this publication.

Brenda Keogh and Stuart Naylor
Millgate House Education, 2008

ii. Essential Information

Each section of the book and CD ROM has support material, with ideas for follow up activities and background mathematical ideas, written in accessible language. Yes, we do give some possible answers!

Concept Cartoons are normally used near the start of the lesson, followed by paired or small group discussion, and then an opportunity to explore or research the ideas being discussed. You do not need long periods of discussion to have an impact on the lesson.

Ask learners to discuss why each character in the Concept Cartoon might hold their particular idea. What might go in the blank speech bubble?

Some Concept Cartoons may initially appear too easy for some learners, but they can provide a useful starting point for discussion about more challenging concepts and often reveal some basic misunderstandings. They can also be used successfully with older learners who lack confidence in mathematics. **If you have the CD ROM you can adjust the level of demand by changing the text.**

Avoid being judgemental when learners are sharing their ideas, as this will close down debate and minimise the development of new ideas and understanding. The uncertainty created by the Concept Cartoons is productive.

The main body of the lesson should provide an opportunity for learners to explore, challenge or consolidate the ideas raised through the Concept Cartoon(s). Allow time at the end of the lesson to share ideas and to consolidate learning. Have they changed their minds and why? Do they want to add new ideas to the Concept Cartoon?

Learners can create their own Concept Cartoons as a way of assessing and reviewing their current understanding.

If you want to know more about Concept Cartoons, and how they are used, please visit:

www.conceptcartoons.com

The Concept Cartoons in this book are also available on an interactive CD ROM. More information about using the CD ROM is available on the following page.

Concept Cartoons in Mathematics CD ROM
(this is available separately)

The CD ROM contains all the Concept Cartoons plus ideas for follow-up and background mathematical ideas, written in accessible language.

The speech bubbles on the CD ROM and many of the central images are fully writeable. **Remember to print out any new Concept Cartoons that you create.**

Using the features on the CD ROM

The writeable speech bubbles allow you to:
- change what the characters are saying
- add learners' ideas to those in the Concept Cartoon
- keep a printed record of learners' ideas
- create new Concept Cartoons
- encourage learners to create their own Concept Cartoons for other groups.

The writeable central images allow you to:
- change the nature of the Concept Cartoon
- increase the level of demand of the Concept Cartoon
- create more Concept Cartoons around the same basic idea.

The follow up activities allow you to:
- share ways of exploring ideas with learners
- provide more challenges related to the concept being explored
- encourage some learners to work more independently.

The background ideas allow you to:
- encourage learners to think about why the characters hold the alternative ideas
- share possible ways of solving the problem with your learners
- provide more challenges related to the concept being explored
- encourage some learners to work more independently.

Any Concept Cartoons created by using this software are for use by the purchasing organisation only and must not be given, or sold, to other individuals or organisations without prior permission from Millgate House Education.

iii. Background Information

> ' Concept Cartoons are cartoon-style
> drawings that put forward a range
> of viewpoints about the mathematics
> involved in everyday situations. '

They are designed to intrigue, to provoke discussion and to stimulate mathematical thinking. By offering different ways of looking at a situation, Concept Cartoons make concepts problematic and provide a stimulus for developing ideas further. They do not always have a single right answer. The outcome may depend on circumstances, definitions and contextual factors. Although some parallels can be found in the research literature, we believe that Concept Cartoons are a unique approach to teaching, learning and assessment.

Our research (Keogh and Naylor, 1999) identifies a number of features that help to make Concept Cartoons effective. These include:

- visual representation of ideas
- minimal text, in dialogue form
- using familiar situations
- offering alternative viewpoints, including the most mathematically acceptable idea(s)
- common areas of misunderstanding, drawn from research and professional practice
- giving the alternatives equal status

How are
Concept Cartoons used?

Concept Cartoons are used in a variety of ways and in a wide range of settings. The most common reasons for using them are:

- making the learners' ideas explicit
- challenging and developing the learners' ideas
- illustrating alternative viewpoints
- providing a stimulus for discussion and argument
- promoting thinking and reasoning
- helping learners to ask their own questions
- providing starting points for mathematical investigation and enquiry
- creating a sense of purpose for the rest of the lesson
- promoting involvement and enhancing motivation
- posing open ended problems
- as extension or consolidation activities
- as a summary of a topic or revision
- outside lesson time (e.g. homework)

> ' Concept Cartoons are often used at the start of a lesson
> or topic as a stimulus for discussion, to identify areas of
> uncertainty and questions to be answered. '

Concept Cartoons are generally used to start the learning process, but they can be used partway through, or at the end of a lesson or topic, where the emphasis is on consolidating learning and applying learning in a new situation. A short period of individual reflection on a Concept Cartoon before discussion starts can be useful for clarifying ideas; similarly some individual follow up after discussion and/or enquiry can be useful for consolidating learning.

> ' Teachers and student teachers also use Concept Cartoons
> for developing their own subject knowledge, by asking questions
> that they may not have thought of asking themselves. '

Introduction

Research shows that many of the misconceptions held by children are retained into adulthood if they are left unchallenged. So as well as identifying the misconceptions and uncertainties that learners may have, teachers can use Concept Cartoons as a mechanism for reviewing their own understanding, identifying their own uncertainties, and ensuring that they can justify which alternatives are correct.

> 'In each Concept Cartoon on the CD ROM, all the speech bubbles and many of the central features are writeable, to enable teachers and learners to create their own Concept Cartoons. The blank speech bubble allows learners to add their own ideas.'

The writeable bubbles allow learners to add ideas and to include the mistakes that they think other people might make. Learners can create their own Concept Cartoons to illustrate possible areas of confusion in a topic. Teachers can create their own Concept Cartoons to change the level of demand, or explore new concepts in the same situation.

Concept Cartoons and talk

Several features of Concept Cartoons help to promote talk between learners:

- The visual stimulus that, for many learners, is more engaging than a written or verbal stimulus

- The limited amount of text, which makes them especially suitable for learners with poor literacy skills

- The cartoon-style format and everyday setting give a strong message of familiarity, making the situations seem accessible

- Presenting ideas in deceptively simple situations promotes engagement with those ideas

- The dialogue between the characters seems to draw learners into their conversation, almost as though the learners are participating in their debate.

> 'Although Concept Cartoons can be used individually, the interaction between learners is important.'

The value of encouraging learners to argue about their ideas is becoming more widely recognised in schools. Teachers may have some concerns about managing this interaction, but using Concept Cartoons enables argument to take place in a controlled and purposeful way. Concept Cartoons provide a focus, a context and a purpose for discussion, and they legitimise argument between learners. This kind of talk supports learning (Alexander, 2006). Having to justify one's ideas to other learners in the group is a powerful mechanism for developing deeper understanding.

> ' Using Concept Cartoons helps learners who
> lack confidence to share their ideas. '

Having different characters putting forward the various alternatives helps to raise the status of each of the alternatives. The threat to a learner's self-esteem from putting forward incorrect ideas is therefore reduced. Having voices speaking for them helps to engage learners who may be reluctant to put forward their own ideas in case they are wrong. After all, if they are wrong then they can blame the cartoon character for putting forward that idea!

Concept Cartoons
and learning

> ' The potential of generating cognitive conflict means that Concept
> Cartoons can be useful for all learners, including those who already
> appear to understand the mathematics involved in the situation. '

All of the alternatives in each of the Concept Cartoons are of equal status. There are no contextual clues, such as facial expressions or one character always having the best understanding, so all the learners are likely to experience cognitive conflict and find that their ideas are challenged. Engagement with a Concept Cartoon can lead to clarification of ideas, more secure learning and translation of knowledge into deeper understanding. One useful approach is to invite learners to work out why each of the characters might think that their idea is correct.

Using Concept Cartoons has implications for the role of teachers and learners in the classroom. In most classrooms, learners put forward ideas and the teacher evaluates them. However, with Concept Cartoons alternative ideas are presented to the learners and they adjudicate between the alternatives. This is a fairly fundamental shift in role.

> ' Even though the teacher has the overall responsibility for managing learning, Concept Cartoons give learners more responsibility in the process and the value of their active involvement is enhanced. '

One very significant aspect of Concept Cartoons is motivation. As teachers we know that motivated learners are more effective learners, and that if learners are disaffected or alienated then there is often little real learning taking place. In our experience, teachers using Concept Cartoons consistently find that their learners are more motivated and engaged.

Concept Cartoons, assessment and learning

> ' Concept Cartoons help to put the principles of assessment for learning into practice. '

Concept Cartoons can be used for individual summative assessment. However they are probably more valuable as an assessment for learning tool, in which assessment is used to make learning more effective (Black and Wiliam, 1998; Black et al, 2002; Hodgen and Wiliam, 2006). As learners make their ideas public, the teacher is able to make informal judgements about their ideas. It quickly becomes apparent whether learners have a good grasp of the basic concepts involved, are struggling to make sense of the situation or hold firmly held but misguided beliefs. The teacher can then take these ideas into account as the lesson progresses.

Meanwhile learners have the opportunity to discuss their ideas and to become more aware of what they and their peers think. Concept Cartoons encourage vigorous discussion and debate, and sometimes this can be enough to change a learner's ideas. More frequently, the discussion raises the need for further investigation or research and begins the process of developing the learner's ideas. In this way using Concept Cartoons for assessment provides a starting point for learning and helps learners create their own learning agenda.

> ' Concept Cartoons identify what learners understand,
> and create the need for further enquiry and learning
> to resolve the conflict between ideas. '

The strength of this connection between assessment and learning was brought home to us when a teacher phoned late one evening to discuss a problem that she had:

> " *I've been using Concept*
> *Cartoons for assessment but*
> *I seem to be doing something*
> *wrong. When I use the Concept*
> *Cartoons I can't stop the children*
> *learning. What should I do?* "

We have used the term 'Active Assessment' to describe this connection, in which purposeful, thought-provoking assessment activities become an integral part of the learning process (Naylor, Keogh and Dabell, 2008). Concept Cartoons are not the only active learning approach to assessment. White and Gunstone (1992) also give excellent descriptions of a range of techniques which can be used in a similar way. However Concept Cartoons are particularly effective at getting learners thinking about their own ideas and how they might need to develop. They promote metacognition - in other words, they help learners to think about their own learning. Even quite young children have commented on how Concept Cartoons make them think about their own ideas and those of other people.

> ' The realisation that there might be lots of ways of thinking
> about a situation can be a powerful incentive to taking other
> people's ideas more seriously. '

Getting learners to create Concept Cartoons for their peers or for younger learners is a good way of assessing their current understanding. They will need to think of possible alternatives as well as ensuring that they have included the mathematically acceptable ideas. This can be quite challenging and revealing!

When we first generated Concept Cartoons, we believed that we would need to target them at particular ages. Experience has taught us that this is not necessarily true, and that many of the Concept Cartoons can be suitable for a very wide age range. Some of the Concept Cartoons originally designed for use with young children have been used successfully with older learners and adult learners; the converse is also true.

> ' Sometimes learners can tackle a Concept Cartoon at their own
> level of understanding, and interpret the problems raised in
> different ways according to their individual starting points. '

The same Concept Cartoon may sometimes be used on more than one occasion and still provide a suitable level of challenge. The blank speech bubbles, and writeable central features on the CD ROM, add to the scope of many of the Concept Cartoons.

Introduction

Introduction

1 Place Value and Understanding Number

Number plate

Play a digit game. In pairs, make up a number, e.g. 1683. Shuffle some 0 - 9 digit cards and place them face down. One person turns over a card. If this matches any of the numbers then add the place and face value of this number to get the score. For example, if 8 is turned over, this scores 88 because in 1683 the digit 8 has a place value of 80 and a face value of 8. Take turns until all the numbers are used, then add the scores to find a winner. Look for numbers in real life where the place value is important and ones where it isn't.

Every number is made up of digits. 762 is made up of three digits 7, 6 and 2. Each digit has two values, its face value and its place value. The face value of the 7 is just 7 because this means the value of the digit itself. The place value of the 7 in 762 is 700 because it is in the hundreds column. In most numbers, knowing the place value is important. However there are some numbers, such as mobile phone numbers and car registration plates, where the place value is not important. Why do we use numbers if the place value isn't important?

1.2

They all add up

Play the following game in pairs to practise rounding skills. Shuffle some 0 - 9 cards and place them in a pile, face down. Each player takes three cards and places them in the order that they appear. The cards are rounded to the nearest hundred and that number of points is scored. For example, if the number made is 261, then this would be rounded to give a score of 300. The player with the highest score after 10 turns is the winner. Try rounding other numbers, including decimals.

Rounding numbers is another way of saying approximately. Numbers can be rounded to the nearest ten, hundred, thousand, and so on. To decide whether to round up or down, look at the number one place to the right. For example, if rounding to the nearest hundred look at the tens column. If the digit is five or more, round up, and if the digit is less than five, round down. So 4549 rounded to the nearest hundred is 4500. Looking in the wrong column is an easy mistake to make. Starting at the units column would give the answer 4550, or looking at the hundreds column would give 5000, but these are not correct. How do we round decimal numbers?

1.3

What's next?

Use a ruler to help with this question. Look at the nine increment lines that show how many millimetres there are between 0 and 1. Imagine that there were more increment lines between 0.9 and 1. Drawing a number line will help. Talk about what these numbers could be. Then draw a new number line and mark 0.91 at one end and 0.92 at the other. Talk about what the numbers between 0.91 and 0.92 could be. Use a decimal number line tool on an interactive whiteboard to explore other number lines.

On a simple number line the next number after 0.9 is likely to be 1 or 1.0. However, this isn't the only number it could be. In between 0.9 and 1.0 there are lots of other numbers, such as 0.91, 0.945, 0.9882, and so on. In fact, there is an infinite number of answers between 0.9 and 1. Which number comes next will depend on how many divisions are included on the number line. Some people may think the answer is 0.10, because 10 comes after 9, but this is not correct. What is the next number after 0.09?

1.4

Double trouble

Write out the column headings units, tenths, and hundredths on a wipeboard and discuss what these mean. Talk about what the decimal point does. You could try adding the amounts by using measuring cylinders. Pour 0.55 L of water into each of two measuring cylinders. Now add the two lots of water together and talk about how much water that makes. Think about the decimals that you have added together. In pairs choose other amounts, such as 0.66 L, or 0.707 L, and challenge other pairs to double them.

When adding two decimals together it is important to understand the value of each digit. For each place to the right of the decimal point, the value becomes ten times smaller. 0.1 means one tenth or $\frac{1}{10}$, 0.01 means one hundredth or $\frac{1}{100}$ and so on. A common mistake is to read the digits after the decimal point as if they are whole numbers. Simply doubling them to get 0.110 L is the wrong answer. Another error would be to ignore the decimal point which will give the incorrect answer 110.0 L. Adding 0.55 L and 0.55 L will make 1.1 L. What happens when you subtract decimal numbers?

Say what?

Write out a list of decimal numbers on a place value chart and practise saying them out loud. For example, 0.7 is read as seven tenths or zero point seven, 0.04 is read as four hundredths or point zero four, 3.002 is read as 3 and two thousandths or three point zero zero two, and so on. Practise reading decimal numbers using data from the Guinness Book of Records or the sports pages of newspapers or websites. For example, search the internet for a favourite sports team and look at the top of the page for how long it takes a search engine to find all the websites, then read out the time.

Reading times can be confusing. For example, some sports commentators say athletics times incorrectly, which can cause misunderstanding about how decimals should be read. Some people may read 10.15 as ten point fifteen, but this is incorrect because the digits do not represent the whole number 15. It is also easy to read the decimal as a fraction so that 10.15 seconds becomes ten and one fifteenth. This is not correct. The stopwatch time shown is read as ten point one five. It can also be read as ten and fifteen hundredths. How would you read a number such as 1.000 01?

On your marks

Write all the race time numbers into a place value table. Then compare the different place values in the numbers. Start with the tenths place and then the hundredths place. For example, compare 15.75 with 15.57 and focus on the tenths digit. The tenths digit in 15.75 is bigger than the tenths digit in 15.57. If the tenths digit is the same, look at the hundredths digit. Compare the other numbers and put them in a table of results, from first place to fifth place. Investigate other decimal numbers, such as temperatures and weight.

When trying to decide if one number is bigger than another start by looking at the whole number. If that is the same, as in this problem, then we look at the number after the decimal point. When comparing decimal numbers, one with a higher number in the tenths place (next to the decimal point) is bigger than one with fewer tenths. If the tenths are equal, then the hundredths place decides which is the bigger number. In a race, the fastest time will be the smallest number. The fastest time in this Concept Cartoon is the time with the smallest digit in the tenths column, which is 15.07 seconds. So Robyn had the fastest time and won the race. What is the difference between the fastest and slowest time?

1.7

Check it out

Find out more about grams and kilograms. How many grams are there in one kilogram, one and a half kilograms (1.5 kg), etc? Use a place value table to work out the weight. Start off with 6.5 kg, write it in the place value table, and read this together, i.e. six kilograms and five hundred grams. Then write in 6.05 kg, and read this as six kilograms and fifty grams. Then write 6.005 kg. What weight will this be? Practise reading baggage weights, such as those in the table.

Number	Read this as
14.1 kg	
8.12 kg	
27.07 kg	
19.303 kg	

Invent some more airport baggage weights and give these to another group to try.

It is very easy to make a mistake if kilograms are shown as decimal numbers. Some people think that 1.5 kg means one kilogram and 5 grams but this is not correct. Other people will read 1.05 kg as 1 kilogram and 5 hundred grams because they say that the 5 is in the hundredths column, but this is not correct either. In the number 6.005 kg, the 6 means 6 kilograms and the .005 means 5 thousandths of a kilogram. A thousandth of a kilogram = 1 gram, so 6.005 kg is 6 kilograms and 5 grams. How much is 6.0005 kg?

1.8

Scored

Play a game using two-digit numbers that cross the hundreds boundary. Each group of 3 or 4 players has 24 digit cards with four of each digit from 4 to 9. One player lays out six cards face up, to form a 3-digit + 3-digit sum, for example 869 + 575. That player works out the total. Then the other players do the same with their cards. When all the players have an answer, everyone checks the answers on a calculator. Each correct answer gets 2 points. The first player to reach 20 points is the winner. Play the game again, but put a zero in each number to make a 4-digit + 4-digit sum, for example, 8069 + 5750.

It is easy to make mistakes when adding across the tens, hundreds or thousands boundaries, particularly when there are zeros in the numbers. Rounding numbers helps to estimate the approximate size of an answer. In this sum 5904 can be rounded up to 6000, and 5106 can be rounded down to 5000. The approximate answer must be in the region of 11 000. The precise answer is 11 010. What other four digit numbers add together to give answers that contain only ones and zeros?

Investigate some divisibility tests and find examples of each. They could be recorded in a table.

Divisibility tests	Example
A number is divisible by 6 if it is divisible by 2 and it is divisible by 3.	168 is divisible by 6 because it is divisible by 2 and it is divisible by 3.
A number is divisible by 8 if the number formed by the last three digits is divisible by 8.	
A number is divisible by 4 if ...	

A common mistake is to think that all numbers ending in 4 are divisible by 4. In this example, 74 doesn't divide exactly by four. Some numbers ending in four do divide evenly by four. For example, 24, 64, 144. If the last two digits of a number are 00 or a multiple of 4, then the number is divisible by 4. For example, 1000 is divisible by 4 because the last two digits are 00. Similarly, 3728 is a multiple of 4 because 28 is a multiple of 4. Does the same rule apply with other numbers? Is 4721 divisible by 7?

Investigate some examples of adding two odd numbers. What is the pattern? Is the answer always even, or does it depend on the numbers being added? Now investigate whether adding three, four, five or six odd numbers makes a difference. What about adding odd and even numbers together? Draw up a table of odd and even rules for adding, subtracting and multiplying. For example,

Addition	Subtraction	Multiplication
Even + even = even	Even − even = even	Even x even = even
Odd + odd = ?	Odd − odd = ?	Odd x odd = ?
Even + odd = ?	Even − odd = ?	Even x odd = ?
Odd + even = ?	Odd − even = ?	Odd x even = ?

The simplest sum of two odd numbers is 1 + 1 = 2. In this example odd + odd = even. It is the same pattern for all the other sums. An odd number can be written as an even number plus 1. For example, A + 1, B + 1, and so on. A, B, are even numbers such as 4 and 6. When we add two odd numbers together, we are adding an even number plus one to another even number plus one. So the sum of any two odd numbers can be written as (A + 1) + (B + 1), which is the same as A + B + 2. Because A and B are both even, A + B + 2 must be even. In other words, two odd numbers added together will always make an even number. Try replacing A and B by even numbers to try it out. What happens if three, four or more odd numbers are added together?

1.11
Zero hero

Investigate what happens when adding an even number to an even number. What is the pattern? Do the same for adding two odd numbers. What is the pattern? Now find out what happens when adding a negative even number to a positive even number, e.g. -2 + 2. Then try adding a negative odd number to a positive odd number, e.g. -3 + 3. Does this show that zero is an even number? Do a websearch to find out what other people think about zero.

It is easy to think zero isn't really a number because you can't have zero of something. However, it belongs to the set of numbers called integers. A web search shows that there is some debate about whether zero is odd or even. This depends on how an even number is defined. Most commonly used definitions of even numbers do include zero as an even number. People also have discussions whether one is a prime number. Find out what they think.

1.12
Square play

Draw a 40 cm by 30 cm rectangle on some large squared paper and then cut out some 5 cm squares. Make enough to cover one side of the rectangle, fit them inside and work out how many would be needed to cover the whole area. Try other shapes and sizes. Discuss what would happen if the rectangle is 96 cm by 60 cm. Create another play area problem using different measurements for another group to try.

There are several ways to solve this problem, so there isn't just one answer. It would be possible to cover the play area in 3, 4 or 6 m squares, or a combination of squares. For the squares to fit exactly, they must be one of the factors of both 60 and 96. The factors of 96 are 1, 2, 3, 4, 6, 8, 12, 16, 24, 32, 48 and 96, and the factors of 60 are 1, 2, 3, 4, 5, 6, 10, 12, 15, 20, 30 and 60. The only common factors are 1, 2, 3, 4, 6 and 12. What if the dimensions of the squares of grass were not whole numbers e.g. 1.5 m squared?

Can can

One way of solving this problem is to actually draw the cans row by row on a mini-whiteboard. In a 10 row stack, there will 1 + 2 + 3 + 4 + 5 + 6 + 7 + 8 + 9 + 10 cans. Is there a quicker way to add together consecutive numbers? For example, focus on pairs of numbers that add up to 10, then count how many of these number pairs there are. Are there other methods of solving the problem? Investigate other stack problems (lists of consecutive numbers) and create some for another group to try.

One possible mistake is to multiply the ten cans in the stack by 10 to make 100 cans because there are ten layers or rows. Another is to multiply the four cans on the bottom row in the picture by 10. However, it isn't possible to work out the number of cans by a simple multiplication sum. Ten rows will contain 55 cans. A quick way to work this out is 1 + N (the quantity of consecutive numbers or rows) x N/2. For the stack of cans we get (1 + 10) x 10/2 = 55. Try to find out why this quick method works. Does this method work for any list of consecutive numbers?

Big school

One way of solving this problem is to use a strategy called guessing and checking. This means starting with an intelligent guess, then checking to see how close it is. The best way to do this is to systematically record all the guesses and results in a table. For example,

Guess	Boys	Girls	Total	Assessment
1	200	237	437	Too low
2	300			
3	400 etc			

Are there other ways to work this out? How can mistakes be avoided? Share ideas between groups. Create some more problems like this to solve and share them between groups. Which is the quickest way to solve the problem?

One possible mistake is to subtract 37 from 757 to make 720. Another possible mistake is to add 37 to 757 to make 794. One way of working out the answer involves subtracting 37 from 757 to get 720, then halving this to give 360 boys. If there are 37 more girls than boys, then there must be 397 girls, so 360 boys + 397 girls = 757 pupils. How many girls would there be if there were 99 more boys than girls? What is the fastest time taken to solve this problem?

1

Place Value and Understanding Number

1.1 Number plate

What do YOU think?

1.2 They all add up

What do YOU think?

1.3 What's next?

What do YOU think?

1.4 Double trouble

What do YOU think?

1.5 Say what?

What do YOU think?

1.6 On your marks

What do YOU think?

1.7 Check it out

What do YOU think?

1.8 Scored

What do YOU think?

1.9 Run to it

What do YOU think?

1.10 That's odd

What do YOU think?

1.11 Zero hero

What do YOU think?

1.12 Square play

What do YOU think?

1.13 Can can

What do YOU think?

1.14 Big school

What do YOU think?

2 Addition and Subtraction

Fruit salad

Share ideas for how to spend the £2. Think about how to check if the amounts are correct. What if there was £3 or £4.50 to spend? Which fruits can be bought now? What is the largest number of fruits that can be bought? What is the smallest number? Include some more fruits at different prices and see if other groups can decide what to buy. Try other fruit salad problems, such as three fruits for the price of two, or price reductions on some fruits.

In this problem, with exactly £2 you can buy 8 apples; or 4 bananas and 4 oranges; or 5 bananas, 1 orange, 1 apple and 1 kiwi. Checking by estimating can help to show if the answer is right. For example, kiwis cost nearly 40p. There are 5 x 40p in £2, but each kiwi is 3p less than 40p so 5 kiwis will not cost exactly £2. It is important not to spend too much. If there is £2 to spend, then 3 kiwis and 4 apples will cost too much even though the answer is close to £2. What common mistakes might people make when adding numbers together to decide which fruit they can buy?

Chocs away

The answer to this problem may seem easy, so why would someone get it wrong? Talk in pairs about the different ways to work out the answer. Think about how to avoid getting the wrong answer. Share ideas with other people in the class. Invent some Concept Cartoons with harder addition sums, where the answers are already worked out. Include a mixture of correct and incorrect answers. Can other groups spot the mistakes that have been made and why? Make a poster to remind each other about what to do in addition sums when the answer crosses the tens boundary.

It is easy to confuse tens and units. This is what the person has done to get 1113p. He has probably added the units, 6 + 7 = 13. Then he has added the tens, 9 + 2 = 11 but, because there is already a 1 in the tens column, he has put the 11 next to it. So he thinks the answer is 1113p. There are other reasons why the people might have got the wrong answer. It is important to remember that the 1 in 13 is a ten to get the right answer, which is 123p. Would they have made the same mistakes if they had used a number line?

2.3
Total it

The answer to this problem may seem easy, so why would someone get it wrong? Look carefully at the different ways that they are trying to work out the answer. Play a follow my leader game by starting off with a sum, e.g. 36 + 9 = ? One person answers and says how they worked out the answer. Then that person passes the answer plus a single digit number to the next person and so on. How many different ways of working out an answer are there? Which ones seem to work well? If anyone is stuck with their sum they can phone a friend to ask for help.

It is easy to forget which numbers are tens and which are units. Another mistake is to use rounding, but to forget whether to add or subtract the difference between the rounded numbers and the real numbers. Rounding is one way to find an answer. 38 + 39 is almost 40 + 40, and 40 + 40 = 80. The difference between 38 and 40 is 2 and the difference between 39 and 40 is 1. Then add 1 + 2 which equals 3 and take this off 80, so 80 − 3 = 77. There is more than one way of solving this sum. Which methods seem to be the most helpful? What mistakes might people make if they use a number line?

2.4
Add this

Spotting mistakes quickly is important. Look at the numbers in this addition sum. Is 9132 a sensible answer? A useful way of checking an addition sum is to turn it round (perform an inverse operation). For example, 124 + 235 = 359 can be checked by doing 359 − 124 or 359 − 235. If the answer is 235 or 124 then the addition is correct. Play an addition card game with a group of players. Mix together two sets of 0-9 digit cards. The referee turns over three cards to make a three-digit number and then turns over another three cards to make another number. The players add these numbers together and each writes their answer on a mini-whiteboard. The referee checks the answers on a calculator by using an inverse operation.

It is easy to make a mistake when carrying twice. Rounding the numbers up or down can help. Round 869 up to 900, and round 163 up to 200. Because 900 + 200 = 1100, the answer must be less than 1100. The problem appears to be in the tens column, where 13 has been written instead of 3. The correct answer is 869 + 163 = 1032. Using different colours for units, tens, etc. can act as a reminder for digits that have been carried forward. What advice could be given to someone to help them to avoid errors crossing the tens and hundreds boundaries?

Playing tiddlywinks is like using a number line. This line is in metres but the people are talking about centimetres. The problem is easier to solve when all the measurements are in centimetres. Use a place value table to convert metres into centimetres.

Th	H	T	U	.	t	h	th
			0	.	8	5	
				.			

To convert metres into centimetres, move the digits two places to the left. Practise this a few times with different measurements. Try playing a conversion game. List some centimetre measurements and challenge another group to write them as metres. Use a centimetre tape measure or measuring stick to play tiddlywinks and work out how far has been jumped and how much further to go. What are the best ways to check the distances?

It is easy to make mistakes when adding decimal numbers by ignoring the zero. Converting from metres to centimetres can also be a problem. In the tiddlywinks game the number line goes from zero to 2 metres or 200 centimetres. The first jump is 40 cm (0.4 m x 100), the next is 85 cm (0.85 m x 100), and the last is 6 cm (0.06 m x 100). 40 cm + 85 cm + 6 cm = 131 cm. To add these numbers on a number line we might jump 40, then 80, then 5, then 6. The distance left to the cup is 200 cm − 131 cm = 69 cm. Which ways could we use to jump from 131 to 200?

Use a number line which shows positive and negative numbers between -30 and +30. Put all the city temperatures on the number line. Look at all the possible pairs of cities. Are there any pairs where the difference is 14 degrees? Using an interactive thermometer is a fun way of counting and showing difference in temperature. A web search will produce an example of an interactive thermometer that can be downloaded. Now explore other positive and negative numbers and work out the difference between them.

A common mistake is to ignore the integer signs and look for two numbers with a difference of 14, such as Mumbai and Helsinki. Another common mistake is to ignore the integer signs and look for two numbers with a total of 14, such as Moscow and Beijing. In this example, the difference between London and Moscow is 14 degrees. The difference between New York and Tokyo is also 14 degrees. Which cities have the greatest difference and the smallest difference between the temperatures?

2.7
Dated

Find out more about BC and AD using books or an internet search. Include the abbreviations BCE and CE in the search. One way to solve this problem is to create a human time line with people holding cards saying the decades between 99 and 1 BC and 1 and 99 AD. Where are BC and AD on the line? What goes between them? Where would 85 BC and 1100 AD be? Extend the time line if necessary. Now try to work out how many years there are between 85 BC and 1100 AD. Invent some more BC and AD problems to share between groups. Does everyone get the same answer?

In the Christian calendar, the letters BC mean before Christ, and the letters AD mean after Christ's birth (it's from the Latin, Anno Domini - in the year of our Lord). Nowadays the terms Common Era and Before Common Era (abbreviated to CE and BCE) are also used. Starting at the left hand end of the time line, the BC or BCE dates count down like the minus numbers on a number line. This means that 100 BC is further in the past than 10 BC. The AD or CE dates run forwards. To find the difference between the two dates, add 1100 and 85 to get 1185 years. How many centuries are there between when the two coins were made?

2.8
Receipt

Find items that are roughly £1, £2 or £5 and round the cost up or down. Find items that group together to make easy numbers to add. Then use these to make an estimate of the total cost and the amount of change due. Use a pencil and paper method to work out the answers, then check using a calculator. Collect shopping receipts and use estimating, grouping and paper methods to check the balance and the change. How well did the estimating work? Create receipts for groups to share with each other. Vary the items and the amount of money used to pay the bill.

Checking receipts for mistakes is worthwhile. When there are several items to add, it is helpful to have a method of quick checking. Rounding and grouping the numbers is a good way to estimate. In this example five numbers can be rounded: £1.99, £0.99, £3.98, £2.05 and £4.98. Two numbers, £1.19 and £1.39, can be grouped to give approximately £2.50. So the approximate total is £16.50. This means that the change is going to be close to £3.50. The correct answer is £3.43. Mistakes can be made when using a calculator, for example £0.99 could be keyed in as £99. When using a pencil and paper method, it is easy to make mistakes where numbers need to be exchanged or carried. What sort of mistakes might be made?

Give me a sign

A number line could be used to work out the distance between the towns. The signpost will be at zero on the number line. Place both towns on the number line and think about how far apart they are. Try playing a signpost game using some 0-9 digit cards. Shuffle them together and deal out two cards. This number is the distance for Town A. Deal out three more cards. This number is the distance for Town B. Now work out the distance between them. Does everyone get the same answer?

Imagine the signpost as zero. Bunbury is at 59 miles. If we count on another 128 miles, we come to Muckle which is 187 miles from zero. This means that Muckle must be 128 miles from Bunbury, or $187 - 59 = 128$ miles, or $59 + 128 = 187$ miles. A common mistake is to add the two distances together, but the two towns are in the same direction. It is also easy to make subtraction errors. For example, someone could get the answer 132 by taking the 7 in 187 from the 9 in 59, instead of the other way round. Mistakes can be made when exchanging a ten for units to make the sum manageable. What would be the difference in the distance between Bunbury and Muckle if the towns were in opposite directions from each other? How could a number line be used to work out the distance?

The answer to this problem may seem easy, so why would someone get it wrong? Start with the units column. Try different numbers in the space. Which number makes that column balance? Then do the same thing with the tens column, then again with the hundreds column. Don't forget to exchange numbers if necessary. What mistakes might be made? Try more subtraction games with missing numbers. Do this in teams. One team works out a subtraction sum and checks the answer with a calculator, then deletes some of the numbers before passing it to the other team. It's easier to start with three-digit numbers, then try four or five-digit numbers.

A common mistake is to ignore the place value and to see this sum as three separate subtraction sums. However, the subtraction sum in the tens column can only be completed after the sum in the units column has been worked out. Also the subtraction sum in the hundreds column can only be completed after the sum in the tens column has been worked out. The final answer is $757 - 188 = 569$. So the missing numbers are 6 and two 7s. What is the smallest number of digits that can be left in a sum, and still be able to work out the answer?

2.11
Take off

Use a number line to work out different possibilities. Create a table to show all the possible combinations of positive and negative numbers. Share the table with another group. Does everyone agree?

Example	Combination	Bigger, smaller, or the same?
6 + 12 = 18	Positive plus positive	Bigger
	Positive plus negative	?
	Positive plus zero	?
	Positive minus positive	?
	Positive minus negative	?
	Positive minus zero	?
	Negative plus positive	?

A common mistake is to ignore the integer signs and look only at the face value of the number. For example, the face value of 5 is greater than 3, but -5 is a smaller number than -3. This can cause confusion when negative numbers are added together or subtracted. When negative numbers are subtracted from another number, the answer is a bigger number. To subtract a positive number, move left along the number line. To subtract a negative number, move right along the number line. Zero subtracted from any number leaves the same number. What is the answer to 0 − (-5) − 7?

2.12
Totally mental

Try to solve the problem in three or four different ways, such as jumping backwards in tens, adding to the nearest ten, and so on. Use a number line to check if this sum is possible. Talk with a partner about which method worked best. Check the answer with a calculator. Now try solving the same problem using mental arithmetic. Talk about ways of finding the answer. Practise subtracting more large two-digit numbers from smaller ones.

In this example, there is more than one way of solving the subtraction sum. Rounding the numbers up or down makes them easier to work with. For example, rounding 25 down to 20 and 73 down to 70 makes it simpler to work out mentally. Twenty minus 70 gives negative 50 (-50). To compensate, because 25 has been rounded down by 5 and 73 rounded down by 3, we need to adjust the answer by 2 (5 − 3) because we are subtracting. So -50 becomes -48. Think of real life situations where someone might take a bigger number from a smaller number, such as being overdrawn at a bank.

The answer to this problem may seem easy, so why would someone get it wrong? Try to solve the problem in three or four different ways, such as using a number line, decomposition, and so on. Check the answer with a calculator. Work with a partner to decide which ways work best. Think about where mistakes might be made. Practise subtracting three and four-digit sums in real situations. For example, subtract darts scores or the price of items on eBay. Work in small groups to create warning signs to help people avoid making subtraction errors.

Errors in subtraction can happen for several reasons, for example when we exchange tens. This is especially true where decimals are involved. In this sum the 6 in the hundredths column in 34.66 cannot be taken from the 5 in 60.15. A ten needs to be changed to units. This leaves 5 tens behind. One of the units then needs to be changed into tenths. This leaves 9 units behind. Then one of the tenths needs to be changed to hundredths leaving 10 tenths behind. Now the answer can be worked out. It should be 25.49. There are other ways to find the answer including rounding the numbers up or down. What if the sum had been 160.05 − 34.96? Would the hundred have to change into tens first?

The answer to this problem may seem easy, so why would someone get it wrong? Look carefully at the place value of each number. Think about different ways of working out Monty's weight. What mistakes might have been made? Look through the answers and imagine marking them. Try to add helpful comments to each answer. Imagine that Monty has only lost 0.05 kg or 0.005 kg. What would his weight be now? Invent some other weight loss or weight gain problems for Monty, and challenge other groups to solve them. Does everyone agree about the answers?

A common mistake to make is to see 0.5 as a whole number, and to subtract 5 from 15.25 to make 10.25 kg. Another error that is easy to make is to set out a subtraction sum like this. Whichever way is used to work out the answer, it is really important to check which numbers are in the tenths and the hundredths columns. The trick is to make sure that the decimal points are lined up and the numbers are kept in order. Putting in a zero, for example 0.50, will help to line the sum up properly. If the 5 is next to the decimal point then the digit 5 in 0.5 is 5 tenths, not 5 hundredths. What would we do if we had to take 0.5 from 15.255?

$$\begin{array}{r} 15.25 \\ -\quad .5 \\ \hline 15.20 \end{array}$$

2.15
Calculator

Explore what kind of mistakes might be made when typing these numbers into a calculator. What difference do the mistakes make to the answer? Would it help to have both amounts in pounds (decimals)? Try rounding the numbers and estimating the answer. Practise subtracting amounts of money, in a range of situations, with and without using a calculator. For example, subtract the different costs of holidays in a travel brochure, or the price of items on a cost comparison web site. Create some problems with mixed pounds and pence. Share them across groups and then compare the answers. Does everyone agree?

In this example an easy mistake to make is to type 2199p as £2199. Another mistake is to type £3088.50 as £388.50. In any sum involving the use of a calculator it helps to estimate the likely size of the answer. In this case rounding £3088.50 to £3100 and 2199p to £20 gives £3080 as the approximate size of the answer. The actual answer is £3066.51. Without using a calculator, try changing between pence and pounds in subtraction sums and subtracting large numbers with different numbers of decimal places, such as 345.7809 − 31.90995. Then check with a calculator.

2.16
Attendance total

The answer to this problem may seem easy, so why would someone get it wrong? Try to solve the problem in three or four different ways. Check the answer with a calculator. Talk with a partner about which method worked best. What mistakes might have been made? Look in newspapers to collect some attendance figures from sporting events. Find the difference between the attendance figures of different sporting events. Check the answers using a calculator. Try this in groups and turn it into a competition to see which group can work out the difference in attendance most accurately, in the fastest time. What advice would you give to someone to help them to work out subtraction sums like this one?

One common mistake in this calculation is to subtract 28 from 34 to leave 6, then subtract 65 from 907 to leave 842. These two numbers are then joined together to make 6842. Swapping numbers round like this is very easy to do, particularly when trying to work out the answer by mental calculation. Mistakes in changing tens and hundreds are also common. Rounding the numbers up or down can be helpful when working with large numbers to check if answers are sensible. The correct answer is 5158. How far from the right answer is the answer in each speech bubble? Try to work it out without pencil and paper.

2.1 Fruit salad

What do YOU think?

2.2 Chocs away

What do YOU think?

2.3 Total it

What do YOU think?

2.4 Add this

What do YOU think?

2.5 Tiddlywinks

What do YOU think?

2.6 City temperatures

What do YOU think?

2.7 Dated

What do YOU think?

I think you will get £3.43 change

I think you will get £2.43 change

Jed's Corner Shop

Receipt

	£
Cling film	1.99
Eggs	0.99
Bread	1.19
Bananas	3.98
Tomato Sauce	1.39
Sunflower Oil	2.05
Chicken	4.98
Balance Due	____
Cash	20.00
Change	____

I think you will get £5.43 change

I think you will get £4.43 change

2.8 Receipt

What do YOU think?

© Millgate House Publishing

2

2.9 Give me a sign

What do YOU think?

2.10 Digital dilemma

What do YOU think?

2.11 Take off

What do YOU think?

2.12 Totally mental

What do YOU think?

2.13 Blast it!

What do YOU think?

2.14 Heavyweight

What do YOU think?

2.15 Calculator

What do YOU think?

2.16 Attendance total

What do YOU think?

Multiplication and Division

3.1
Times ten

Explore multiplying by 10, 100 or 1000 by acting out a sum. Four people stand at the front of the class, holding digits and a decimal point to make a number - for example 25.3. Make the number ten times bigger (multiply by 10). Decide which way the numbers should move. Have some people with zeros, to help out. Read out the number. Do it again with different numbers.

Sometimes a number can be multiplied by 10 by adding a zero on the end. For example, 9 x 10 = 90. However, this 'trick' doesn't always work. Adding a zero on the end of a decimal number doesn't change the size of the number. For example, 40.50 is the same size number as 40.5. When multiplying by 10 it is much better to move all the digits one place to the left, so 40.5 becomes 405. The decimal point is like a concrete post, it stays in one spot and the digits move past it. What happens to the numbers when you multiply by 100 or 1000?

3.2
Dictionary definition

Start with an easy number such as 4 and explore what happens if you multiply it by zero, by one, by proper fractions (e.g. ½), by improper fractions (e.g. ³⁄₂), by decimals (e.g. 0.2) and by negative numbers (e.g. -2). Share ideas about the answers and whether the product is bigger, smaller or stays unchanged. Look in dictionaries for 'multiply' and 'multiplication'. Discuss how the dictionary definitions could be improved.

Sometimes when multiplying two numbers together, the answer can be a bigger number. For example, 6 x 7 = 42. But sometimes multiplying numbers together makes a smaller answer. For example, 6 x ½ = 3. It depends on which types of numbers are multiplied together. Multiplying a positive whole number by proper fractions, negative numbers or decimals makes a smaller number. Multiplying any number by one gives the same number, for example 1 x 657 = 657. Multiplying any number by zero gives zero, for example 0 x 300 = 0. What happens if you start with a negative number?

3.3

Burger bar

Explore different methods and try to rank them according to how efficient they are. For example, multiply 38 and £1.99 using repeated addition. Compare this method to other methods of multiplication, such as long multiplication, rounding, the grid method, multiplying by factors and so on. Do other groups think the same about which method is most efficient? Try inventing other real life money problems for another group to solve. Create some handy hints for solving money problems.

This problem can be solved in different ways. There is no 'right' way of doing a sum like this, but there might be a method that is more efficient than another. For example, adding £1.99 thirty eight times in a vertical sum is one way, but it would take a long time and it would be easy to make lots of mistakes. Possibly the easiest way to work out this sum is to round £1.99 to £2 by adding 1p, multiply by 38, then subtract the 38 extra pence (38 x 1p) to give a total of £75.62. Does everyone agree that this is the easiest way to work it out?

3.4

Lolliop

Explore the different kinds of mistakes that can be made when multiplying. Work in groups to try to work out the mistakes that these children might have made. Look at which numbers have been multiplied together. Now make a poster that explains how to multiply two 2-digit numbers to avoid making errors. Take some time to think about what to say, then explain the poster to the rest of the class. After everyone has made their presentation, compare what has been said and think about how the posters could be improved.

People forget which number is the unit and which is the ten. It is easy to make a mistake. For example, one person seems to have multiplied 22 by 2p = 44p. Then they multiplied 22 by 1p (instead of 10p) = 22p and added them together to make 66p. Another person seems to have swapped the 1 and the 2 in 12. So we have 22 times 1p = 22p added to 22 times 20p = 440p. Added together they make 462p. Neither of these is the correct answer which is 264p. It is a good idea to know more than one method of multiplying numbers, so that an alternative strategy can be used to double check an answer. What different methods can be used?

Explore some adverts for the latest deals on mobile phones, and compare their tariffs and call charges. Look carefully at what they are offering, and work out which phone appears to be the best deal. Estimate what calls would be made in a typical month, then investigate whether it is better to opt for a pay-as-you-go package or monthly charges. Try to work out the best way of checking the deals.

It's very easy to get confused by phone call charges, when the charges depend on when the calls are made as well as how long they are. In this example, the table shows someone making 148 minutes of calls over the week. Signing up for Deal 1 would cost £18.30 and Deal 2 would cost £19.24. Deal 1 works out to be better value because weekend calls are cheaper, and 78 out of 148 minutes were made at the weekend. Try to work out when Deal 2 would be cheaper.

3

Visit a shop or supermarket and collect examples of multi-pack buys. Log on to an online supermarket and do a survey of multi-pack buys, buy one get one free, or 3 for 2 offers. What's the best way to check which is the best buy? Do value packs always work out as good value for money, or do they sometimes cost more? Report what the survey shows, and what methods are good for checking best buys, to the rest of the class. Create some similar problems for another group to solve.

To check best buys, the price of a single bag needs to be found. A single bag of crisps in the 8 pack costs about 25p (1.99 ÷ 8), in the 12 pack a single bag costs about 22p (£2.69 ÷ 12), and in the 10 pack a bag costs about 21p (£2.09 ÷ 10). The best buy is the 10 pack. Multi-packs in shops are usually the cheapest option, especially when they are advertised as special offers to customers. However, this isn't always the case. Sometimes single items can be cheaper, so being able to calculate the price of one item is a useful skill to have. Rounding numbers can help to do this more easily. Look at special value bottles of drinks. Is the bigger size better value? What's the best way to work it out?

3.7
Music to my ears

Write down the pocket money received by a group of fictitious friends and calculate how long it would take for them to save up for a particular present. Share these with another group to see if everyone agrees about the answers. Sometimes it is possible to buy things over a period of weeks, rather than pay all in one go. Usually the shop will charge more for stretching out the payments. Investigate some advertisements where there is a credit option, and work out how much more it would cost to pay in this way. For example, a bicycle is for sale at £89.90, or 20 weeks at £4.75, or 50 weeks at £1.85.

The number of weeks it would take to save enough money to buy an iPod is 26 weeks, since 26 x £4.75 = £123.50. A common mistake to make is to choose the number of weeks which give the closest amount to £119. So, £4.75 x 25 is almost £119, but is still 25p short of the cost of the iPod. Discuss the methods used to check the answer. For example, partitioning £4.75 into £4 and 75p, then multiplying by the number of weeks, would be one way. How could she work out how many weeks it would take to buy the iPod if she got £9.25 pocket money?

3.8
In pieces

Start with an easy number, such as 10 or 100, and try multiplying by different fractions. Don't forget improper fractions (e.g. $\frac{10}{7}$) and mixed numbers (e.g. $3\frac{3}{8}$). Which ones produce a smaller answer? Which ones produce a bigger answer? Use a calculator to work them out if necessary. Is there an obvious pattern? Does everyone agree? Produce a poster to show what happens with the different types of numbers.

Although the rumour is true much of the time, it isn't always true. Lots of numbers do get smaller when multiplied by a fraction, for example 10 x $\frac{1}{2}$ = 5. However there are some exceptions, depending on which numbers you multiply. These include multiplying by an improper fraction, such as 2 x $\frac{7}{7}$ = 2, or 10 x $\frac{22}{7}$ = $\frac{220}{7}$. In these examples the answer isn't smaller. Multiplying by a mixed number will produce a bigger number, for example, 10 x $4\frac{1}{3}$ = $43\frac{1}{3}$. What about multiplying two fractions together, such as $\frac{1}{4}$ x $\frac{1}{4}$? What about negative numbers?

Choose a period of time, and then compare how much money can be made during that time doing each activity. What if any of the charges change? Here is a weekly sales chart. The car washer works 6 hours a day, and needs to earn £550 a week to get a wage and cover all the costs of the business. Does the business make any money?

Day	Cars Washed	Cars washed and waxed	Cars Valeted	Total
Monday	3	1	1	
Tuesday	5	1	0	
Wednesday	12	8	0	
Thursday	4	6	0	
Friday	7	5	0	
Saturday	25	11	3	

Are there any problems with the chart? What happens if the charges or the numbers of cars change?

If 6 cars are washed in an hour then this makes £22.50, so 2 hours of washing cars every 10 minutes would earn £45. This compares with £40 for 8 wash and waxes, or £40 for a two-hour valet. Of course this assumes that there is a constant queue of cars, and that no time is wasted. So although mathematically this is quite a simple problem, in real life the answer will depend on factors such as the number of customers and the weather conditions. If there is a 2 minute gap between each car, what is the maximum the car washer could earn in 2 hours?

3.10
Smoothie

Try some different word problems, starting with easy numbers. For example, try $\frac{1}{2}$ of 4 and write this in different orders, such as $2 \div 4 \times 1$, or $1 \times 4 \div 2$, or $4 \div 2 \times 1$, or $1 \div 2 \times 4$, and so on. Which order gives the correct answer? Try this with larger numbers and see if the same order always gives the correct answer. Then invent more word problems like this for another group to try. For example, there are 28 children in a class. Five sevenths of the children didn't do their homework. How many children did do their homework?

It is possible to solve $\frac{3}{4} \times 8$ in different ways. It could be solved as $(3 \times 8) \div 4$, or $(8 \div 4) \times 3$, or 0.75×8. All of these give the same answer. Three quarters of 8 is 6 apples. It is important to understand the word 'of' as meaning multiply, so $\frac{3}{4}$ of the apples means multiply the number of apples by $\frac{3}{4}$. Brackets help to organise the numbers and to identify which part of the sum should be worked out first. Does the same order work for improper fractions, such as $\frac{12}{5}$ of 65?

3.11
Through the zoo

Numbers containing zeros can cause confusion. Try dividing 65, 650, 6500, 605, 6050, 60 050 and 600 500 by 5, and write down the answers. Then try dividing 27 270, 2700, 207, 2070, 20 070 and 200 700 by 9, and write down what you get. Compare answers with another group. Do they agree? Is there a pattern? What difference does the zero make? Design a poster showing others how to avoid a zero error, and present the poster to the rest of the class.

A common mistake to make in this calculation is to ignore one or both of the zeros in 5040. 90 and 86 are both too small to be the correct answer. Another mistake in this problem is to work out 5040 divided by 7 days. The notice shows that the zoo is only open for six days of the week. 5040 divided by 6 makes the average attendance 840 per day. Try zero problems using decimal numbers, for example, 8.4, 8.04, 80.04, 800.04 etc divided by 3.

3.12
Take your medicine

Think about number problems using tablets. For example, if the person takes 2 tablets 3 times a day, and the tablets have to last for 5 days, how many should be in the box? Try designing some medicine labels. For example, 'Take no more than 4 tablets in 24 hours, with at least 5 hours between tablets' or 'I tablet every 6 hours' or '2 tablets in the morning and 2 more in the evening'. Decide on the number of tablets per pack. Pass the problem to another group to solve.

Problems can be solved by working systematically. If someone takes 2 tablets 3 times a day, then they take 6 tablets each day. If there are 7 x 24 tablets in the pack, then there are 168 tablets altogether. 168 divided by 6 means the tablets will last 28 days. An easy way to solve this problem is to divide 24 by 6 and then multiply by 7. In real life, people sometimes don't take the correct medication because they confuse the numbers. For example, they may need to think carefully about how many tablets to take, and when, if they read 'Take 2 tablets every 4 hours but no more than 8 in a period of 24 hours'. Try the same problem with volumes of liquid medicine.

Divide time

Explore what happens when dividing a number by one, by proper fractions, by improper fractions, by decimals or by negative numbers. Talk about whether the product is a bigger number, a smaller number or whether it stays unchanged. Do other groups agree? Invent some word problems for other groups to try. For example, 'I have a 5 cm long string and cut it into strips that are each $\frac{1}{3}$ cm long. How many strips will I get?'

Division is commonly thought of as sharing, but there are other meanings as well: equal grouping, repeated subtraction, ratio and so on. Not all examples of division involve numbers getting smaller. Dividing by a fraction will make the number bigger. For example, $10 \div \frac{1}{2} = 20$. This could also be written as 'Cut a pie into 10 equal pieces. Now cut each piece in half. How many pieces are there now?' Dividing any number by one gives the same number, for example $657 \div 1 = 657$. What about dividing by zero?

Rumours

Investigate dividing small numbers by larger numbers, such as $2 \div 4$ or $5 \div 10$. Try it on a calculator. What sort of answer does it give? Now swap the numbers over and compare the answer. Is it bigger or smaller? Is there a pattern? Share ideas with another group. Do they agree? What happens if fractions or decimals are divided?

A possible misconception is that a smaller number cannot be divided by a larger one. It can, and the answer can be given as a decimal or fraction. For example, $2 \div 4 = \frac{1}{2}$ or 0.5. Using a calculator will help to make this more obvious. Division is not commutative. This means that when the numbers are swapped around in a division sum, the answer is not the same. So, $2 \div 5 = \frac{2}{5}$ (or 0.4) and $5 \div 2 = 2\frac{1}{2}$ (or 2.5). If you compare the answers you find that $2 \div 5$ is $6\frac{1}{4}$ (6.25) times smaller than the answer to $5 \div 2$. You can work this out by dividing the square of the large number by the square of the smaller number $(5 \times 5) \div (2 \times 2) = \frac{25}{4} = 6.25$. Why do you think this works? What about fractions and decimals?

3.15
Decimal division

Use a place value table to practise division by 10, 100 and 1000. For example, what does 476.2 become when divided by 10? by 100? by 1000? How will these numbers be written in the table? Try writing out a number of decimal division sums for another group to do.

Th	H	T	U	.	t	h	th
	4	7	6	.	2		
				.			

These could be written as number sums or as number sentences.

Sometimes a number can be divided by 10 just by taking a zero off the end. For example, $94\,760 \div 10 = 9476$, which is the correct answer. However, this 'trick' doesn't always work. Taking a zero off the end of a decimal number doesn't change the size of the number. So $7.40 \div 10$ is 0.74, not 7.4, because the number is ten times smaller. When dividing by 10 it is much better to move all the digits one place to the right. The decimal point is like a concrete post, it stays in one spot and the digits move past it. What happens when a number is divided by 0.10?

3.16
Spudz

Try investigating how many different ways there are for planting a particular number of potatoes and find out if there is a remainder or not. Explore this using 20 potatoes and different numbers of rows. Do the potatoes always fit neatly into the rows? Is there a way to predict if there will be any potatoes left over? Would thinking about factors help? For example, if there are 36 potatoes, what are the factors of 36? What happens if factors are used to decide the number of potatoes in a row?

Planting 140 potatoes in rows of 16 would give 8 rows and 12 left over. 16 is not a factor of 140 so there is a remainder. So Auntie Kat would get some too. If all the potatoes are planted using factors of 140 (that is, 1, 2, 4, 5, 7, 10, 14, 20, 28, 35, 70 or 140) in a row, there will not be a remainder. For example, 2 rows would have 70 potatoes each, 4 rows would have 35 each, and so on. If a factor can be used to decide the number of potatoes in a row there will not be a remainder. What do we call numbers that can make more than one equal row? What do we call numbers that can't?

There are lots of real world examples to try out. For example, the ratio of boys to girls in a class is 2:3. If there are 8 boys, how many girls are there? Bread is made from flour and yeast in the ratio 30 to 1. How much yeast is mixed with 960 g of flour? Concrete is made from 1 shovel of cement, 2 of gravel and 5 of sand. How much sand and gravel is needed for 6 shovels of cement? After practising some examples, think of more versions for other groups to try.

In this example, add 2 and 3 to get 5 to find out how many lots of money will be needed altogether. One share will be £60 ÷ 5 = £12. David gets 3 lots, so his share will be 3 x £12 = £36. His brother gets 2 lots, so his share will be 2 x £12 = £24. Adding £24 and £36 makes £60. This method works in the same way for ratios involving 3 people. So Brian, Stuart and Ellie divided £560 between them in the ratio 2:1:5. How much did Ellie receive? Add 2 + 1 + 5 to get 8, then £560 ÷ 8 = £70. So Brian will get £70 x 2 = £140, Stuart will get £70 x 1 = £70 and Ellie will get £70 x 5 = £350. What would they each get if £560 was divided between them in the ratio 7:20:15?

Start by thinking of small surveys of 10 people. Who likes sugar in their tea and who doesn't? Who likes horror films and who doesn't? Then create more complicated surveys. For example, 5 out of 20 children said that they went to bed after 9 p.m. 100 children were surveyed. How many went to bed before 9 p.m.? Try to create a range of different examples for another group to work out, using different sets of numbers.

An easy mistake to make here is to subtract 30 from 320 to leave 290. If 320 people were surveyed, and 3 out of every 10 said they liked sprouts, then this is a total of 96 people because $\frac{3}{10}$ x 320 = 96. If 96 people do like sprouts, it is easy to work out that 224 people did not like sprouts. These surveys are easiest to make sense of when the choices are either/or and there are no other possibilities. For example, if 4 out of 10 people travel by car, this does not mean that 6 out of 10 travel by train. Some people might walk or cycle, or not travel at all. Carry out a survey and compare people's preferences.

3.1 Times ten

What do YOU think?

3.2 Dictionary definition

What do YOU think?

3.3 Burger bar

What do YOU think?

3.4 Lollipop

What do YOU think?

3.5 On the phone

What do YOU think?

3.6 Best buy

What do YOU think?

3.7 Music to my ears

What do YOU think?

3.8 In pieces

What do YOU think?

3.9 Car wash

What do YOU think?

3.10 Smoothie

What do YOU think?

3.11 Through the zoo

What do YOU think?

3.12 Take your medicine

What do YOU think?

3.13 Divide time

What do YOU think?

3.14 Rumours

What do YOU think?

3.15 Decimal division

What do YOU think?

3.16 Spudz

What do YOU think?

David has won £60 on the lottery. He plans to share the money with his brother in the ratio 3:2

David gets £30, his brother gets £20

David gets £40 and his brother gets £20

David gets £36 and his brother gets £24

David gets £32 and his brother gets £28

LOTTERY

A: 06 09 18 36 39 47

3.17 In the money

What do YOU think?

3.18 Our survey said

What do YOU think?

4 Fractions and Percentages

4.1
I'll have a slice

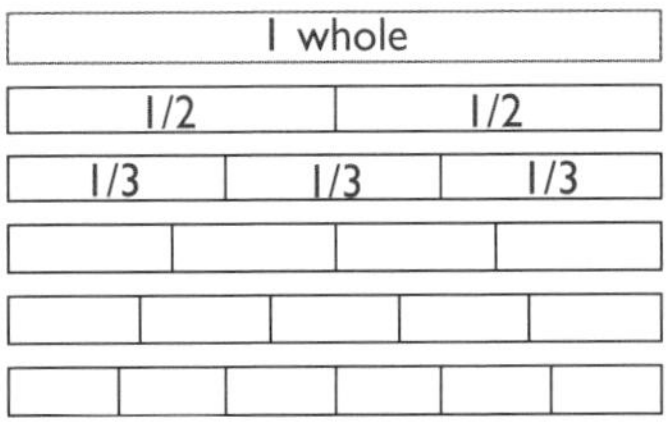

Explore the size of fractions by using a fraction wall. The fraction wall divides rectangles into fractional parts, as shown. This helps to show the size of fractions. Use the fraction wall to investigate whether $\frac{2}{3}$ is bigger than $\frac{1}{4}$ or $\frac{4}{8}$. Invent some fraction challenges for another group to try.

A common mistake is to think that if the bottom number is big, the number is a big number. This isn't correct. In fractions big becomes small. For example, $\frac{1}{16}$ is smaller than $\frac{1}{2}$. Similarly a big top number doesn't mean that the fraction is a big number. It's the relationship between the top and bottom numbers that matters. For example, $\frac{7}{16}$ is smaller than $\frac{5}{8}$. In this example, the biggest fraction is $\frac{2}{3}$. Is $\frac{11}{12}$ bigger or smaller than $\frac{9}{10}$?

4.2
Contain yourself

Explore this problem by acting it out. For example, get two one litre containers marked in fractions, and put $\frac{3}{4}$ L (750 ml) water in one and $\frac{1}{4}$ L (250 ml) water in another. Now add the $\frac{1}{4}$ L water to the container with $\frac{3}{4}$ L. This makes one whole litre (1000 ml) of water in the one litre container. Try repeating this problem with other fractions of a litre, including $\frac{1}{2}$ L + $\frac{1}{4}$ L. Try adding volumes of water in three containers, and inventing statements for other groups to check.

Fractions consist of two numbers. The top number is called the numerator. The bottom number is called the denominator. A common mistake, when adding two fractions, is to add or to multiply the numerators and denominators together (e.g. $\frac{1}{2} + \frac{1}{4} = \frac{2}{6}$, or $\frac{1}{2} + \frac{1}{4} = \frac{2}{8}$). This isn't correct. Where the denominators are the same, the numerators can be added together (e.g. $\frac{1}{8} + \frac{4}{8} = \frac{5}{8}$). Where the denominators are different, they need to be changed so that they are the same. This means choosing a number that can be divided by both denominators. For example, for $\frac{1}{2} + \frac{1}{4}$, both 2 and 4 will divide into 4. So, change one half to two quarters. Now $\frac{2}{4} + \frac{1}{4} = \frac{3}{4}$. What will $\frac{5}{6} + \frac{5}{12}$ make?

4.3
Off we go

What is the difference between $\frac{1}{4}$ **of** the price and $\frac{1}{4}$ **off** the price? Make up some more special offer problems. For example, 25% off digital radios, normal price £60, or T shirts reduced by $\frac{1}{3}$, usual price £7.50. Try some with another group. Do they agree? A 'money off' table will be useful.

Discount	Sale price	Example
$\frac{1}{4}$ or 25%	$\frac{3}{4}$ or 75%	Original cost £36, discount £9, sale price £27
$\frac{1}{2}$		
$\frac{1}{3}$		
$\frac{1}{5}$		
$\frac{1}{10}$		

In this Concept Cartoon, $\frac{1}{3}$ **off** means that the original price is reduced by $\frac{1}{3}$ or approximately 33%. The selling price will now be $\frac{2}{3}$ **of** the original price. A common mistake is to see the amount of the reduction as the actual selling price. But $\frac{1}{3}$ **off** means that it's reduced by $\frac{1}{3}$, not that it sells for $\frac{1}{3}$ **of** the original price. Similarly, 25% **off** means that something is reduced by 25%, not that it sells for 25% **of** the original price. What is the difference, as a percentage, between 15% **off** and 15% **of** the price?

4.4
Sweet tooth

Invent some sweet bag problems using different numbers and fractions. To decide on the fractions, pick two cards from a 0-9 pile. For example, if 6 and 8 are picked the fraction will be $\frac{6}{8}$. Do this twice and compare the two amounts for a bag of 30 and 40 sweets. Which one gives you more sweets? Swap sweet bag problems with another group, and see if each group can agree on which one gives you more sweets.

A common mistake is to see a large denominator (the bottom number) and think of it as a whole number, so when the denominator is big, the number is a big number. This isn't correct. In this problem it is necessary to look at each statement in turn and work out which offers the better deal. The size of the fraction, and the size of the bag of sweets, both make a difference. The character who has made the best choice is the girl choosing $\frac{2}{4}$ of 30 (which is 15 sweets), rather than $\frac{1}{3}$ of 40 (which is 13.33 sweets). Which character has the biggest difference between the two amounts?

Try some more proportion sums. Swap problems with another group and see if each group can agree on which is the biggest or smallest proportion. Try making a list of commonly used percentages, fractions, and decimals. Write these (where possible) in their lowest terms. For example,

A common mistake is to think that a percentage or a decimal is bigger than a fraction, because they contain more digits. In this example, it is easier to think about each number in the same terms. For example, converting each number into a

Percentage	Decimal	Fraction	Lowest term
10%	0.1	$^{10}/_{100}$	$^1/_{10}$
20%			$^1/_5$
25%			
30%			
and so on			

decimal shows that 80% = 0.8, $^1/_3$ = 0.33 (to two decimal places) and $^3/_4$ = 0.75. So the apple contains the biggest proportion of water (0.8). To be accurate, the characters should refer to the proportion of water in the different foods. From their conversation, it looks like they mean proportion, not amount. If they do mean the amount, then this will depend on how big the food items are as well as the proportion of water. Try working out the amount of water for different size food items.

Explore this using a one litre container and filling it completely with water. What percentage of the container is full when it contains 500 ml? 900 ml? 950 ml? 1000 ml? Will it hold another 10% when it already holds 1000 ml? Will it hold another 50%? Look out for examples of giving more than 100% in news stories on the internet, in newspapers and on TV and radio.

In everyday language giving 110% is used to mean try extra hard. So sometimes people will tell us to give 110%, but this is impossible. 100% represents the whole unit, or the whole amount. So 100% must be the maximum effort we can put in. 110% would mean more than the total amount than we can give, or more than the maximum effort, and this isn't possible. Is it possible to find examples where more than 100% is a sensible description of something?

4.7
Fruit pot

Explore simple percentages first, such as 10% of 50. Collect some examples of ingredients in different foods. Work out the percentages, and compare them with other brands of the same products. Do they all have the same percentage of the different ingredients? Why might the percentages be different (e.g. the percentage of sugar in jam or yoghurt)? Invent some fruit pot examples for another group to try. Rather than one percentage amount, list two or three ingredients, such as 25% mango and 55% orange in fruit juice.

12% means 12 out of 100. The 100 is another way of saying the whole thing. In this example, the whole thing is the yoghurt pot which contains 125 g of yoghurt. How much fruit is there in the 125 g of yoghurt? To work this out, divide 12 by 100 and you get 0.12 g (that's the amount in every 1 g of yoghurt) and then multiply this by 125 and you get 15 g. Another way of arriving at the same answer is to do 125 x 12 ÷ 100. Percentage problems like this can always be tackled by breaking them down into more manageable amounts, for example, finding 10% of 125 g = 12.5 g, and then another 2% of 125 g = 2.5 g, then 12.5 + 2.5 = 15 g. Explore other quick ways of finding percentages, including using a calculator.

4.8
Taxing times

Try working out 17.5% VAT in different ways by using a calculator. Are all the answers the same? Try checking the answer by using other methods and compare the answers with the ones on the calculator. Here is one way to work out 17.5% VAT. 10% + 5% + 2.5% = 17.5%, so first find 10% (a tenth) of £168 by dividing by 10. Note the number. Then halve that answer to find 5%. Note that number. Then halve that answer to find 2.5%. Note that number. Finally, add those three numbers together, to give the total amount of VAT. Does everyone get the same answer? Try some more tax problems. For example, a mobile phone is priced at £168 without VAT. What is the VAT? Write some tax problems for another group to try.

In the UK, VAT (Value Added Tax) is 17.5%. How much VAT is added to the cost of the radio? To work this out, enter the following numbers on a calculator: 80 x 17.5 ÷ 100, or 80 x 17.5 then %, to get an answer of £14. This is the amount of tax, so the total cost of the radio, including the tax, is £80 + £14 = £94. Another way of finding the total price is to enter on a calculator 80 x 117.5 then %, or 80 x 1.175. Why does this work? What would the radio cost if the VAT changed to 22.5%?

Try out the problem using cubes or other objects. Does everyone get the same answer? Collect some examples of packaging that show a percentage increase in the amount, and discuss what they mean. For example, if there are usually 12 toilet rolls in a pack, and the label says '25% extra free', how many will there be in the pack? If a bar of chocolate is usually 150 g, and the label says '15% bigger bar for the same price', how big is the extra-size bar? Invent some special offers using different percentage amounts for other groups to solve.

A common mistake is to think that 100% extra means getting 100 times as much. Another easy mistake would be to think it increases by ten times as much or half as much. When we get 100% extra of something, we get twice as much. 100% represents the whole amount, so if a product contains 100% extra then it will contain the same amount again. This is twice as much altogether. Look out for 2 for the price of 1, or 3 for 2 special offers. What percentage extra do you get?

Consider each statement in turn and discuss which statements seem to make sense. Why might people think that any of the answers are correct? What mistakes might they make? Look at a piece of text on a computer and change the text size using the zoom option. Try enlarging some shapes drawn on squared paper by different amounts. Use a photocopier to enlarge or shrink images by different amounts. Try reducing a piece of A4 text by 70%, by 50%, by 35% and see what happens. Try enlarging a piece of A4 text by 140%, by 200%, by 280% and see what happens.

Enlargement does not change the shape of an object, only its size. The object is multiplied by a scale factor to enlarge or reduce the image. For example, a scale factor enlargement of 3 means something gets three times bigger. Enlarging text to 200% means that it will be 200% of its original size – in other words, it gets twice as big or 100% bigger. Is it possible to reduce the size of something by 200%?

4.11
Letting off steam

Investigate whether the order of working out the percentage price cut makes a difference. Decide on a price for the kettle. Try 20% and then 10% off the price. Next try 10% and then 20% off the price. Is there a difference? Is one way better than the other? Try some other problems to see if the rule stays the same. For example, a house costs £140 000 this year. The price goes up 10% next year, then another 5% in the following year. What does it cost in two years time? Would it be different if it went up 5% and then 10%?

A common mistake is to add the percentages together, but the card holder only gets an extra 10% off the sale price, and this is not 30% in total. It is also a mistake to think that it makes a difference whether the 20% or the 10% is taken off first. In fact they both produce the same answer. Suppose that the kettle costs £100 (it's an expensive kettle). Taking 20% off this price takes it down by £20 to £80. Then 10% off the £80 takes it down by £8 to £72. £72 is a 28% reduction off the original price. The 10% reduction is taken off the sale price, not off the original price. This is why the kettle costs £72, not £70. What would the percentage reduction be if the storecard holder got an extra 25% off the sale price?

4.12
Crisp numbers

Explore percentages using 45 cubes or other objects. Does everyone get the same answer? Collect a variety of examples of food labels (including pet foods). Look at the information about nutritional values on the labels. Work out how much they contain of the different types of food. For example, how much salt, sugar, fat and protein is there in a can of beans? In a can of soup? In a frozen pizza? In a chocolate ice cream? Decide whether any of the food labels seem to be misleading, and if so, how.

In this example, 15% of 45 g = 45 × 15 ÷ 100 = 6.75 g of fat in the packet of crisps. On a calculator the sequence will be 45 × 15 then %, or 45 × 0.15. It is easy to mix up grams and percentages. Different kinds of fat, such as saturated, and unsaturated fat, may be listed separately on the label. Reading the information printed on packets of food can help us to make healthy food choices. How much fat would somebody eat if they ate two packets of crisps? How much fat is in a packet of crisps if the percentage is 25%?

How much pizza do you want?
$^4/_8$ $^1/_{15}$ $^2/_3$ $^1/_4$

4.1 I'll have a slice

What do YOU think?

4.2 Contain yourself

What do YOU think?

4.3 Off we go

What do YOU think?

4.4 Sweet tooth

What do YOU think?

4.5 Water surprise

What do YOU think?

4.6 Try your best

What do YOU think?

4.7 Fruit pot

What do YOU think?

4.8 Taxing times

What do YOU think?

4.9 Cuppa time

What do YOU think?

4.10 Getting bigger

What do YOU think?

4.11 Letting off steam

What do YOU think?

If I eat a bag of crisps then I eat 38.25 g of fat

I think you eat 6.75 g of fat

I think you eat 3 g of fat

I think you eat 15 g of fat

crisps

45 g

5%	Protein
74%	Carbohydrate
15%	Fat
3%	Fibre
3%	Other

4.12 Crisp numbers

What do YOU think?

Shape

Draw what each shape might look like. Compare drawings and talk about each one. Which ones are different? Now use different dictionaries and explore how a square is described. Also look at the definitions for a parallelogram, rhombus, kite and rectangle. What do they say? How do they match your shapes? Look for examples of the shapes around your classroom and school. Create a shape dictionary for the class.

People often know that a square is a quadrilateral or a four-sided regular polygon, but it can be described in other ways. It could be described as an equilateral quadrangle or a tetragon. A square is also an example of a special parallelogram and rectangle with equal parallel sides and angles of 90°. It is also possible to find a square called a special case of a rhombus or kite. Can other shapes be described in more than one way?

Read each of the statements and draw what each shape might look like. Compare drawings and talk about each one. Does everyone agree? Consult some dictionaries and look for the definitions of equilateral, isosceles, acute-angled, and scalene triangles. Can the definitions be made clearer? Design a poster about different triangles and where and how they are used. Hold a poster conference in class. Display them around the class with a blank sheet next to each one for comments.

The flag is an equilateral triangle. It is a three-sided polygon with three equal sides. It may come as a surprise to know that it can also be described as an isosceles triangle. An isosceles triangle is a triangle with at least two equal sides and angles. So that makes an equilateral triangle a special case of an isosceles triangle, because it has three equal sides and three equal angles. It is also an acute-angled triangle, because each of its angles is less than 90 degrees. It can also be called an oblique triangle. In a scalene triangle all the angles are different. Where are scalene triangles found?

5.3
Check mate

To understand this problem start by looking at a 2 x 2 square and counting all the possible squares (5). Then explore progressively bigger squares up to 8 x 8. It helps to use a systematic method of working to find the total number of squares. This could be set out in a table.

A common mistake is to count each individual square on a chessboard and think that there are 64 squares. In fact there are 204 squares. In addition to the 64 single squares there are all the 2 x 2 squares, all the 3 x 3 squares, and so on up to the 8 x 8 square. These can be written as square numbers, so 1 + 4 + 9 + 16 + 25 + 36 + 49 + 64 = 204. What would be the next numbers in the pattern? Where are these patterns seen in everyday life?

Size	Total number of squares
1x1	1
2x2	1 + 4 = 5
3x3	1 + 4 + ? = ?
4x4	
5x5	
6x6	
7x7	
8x8	

5.4
Give us a ring

How many examples of each shape can be seen in the classroom? Around the school? In the street? In the wider world? Examples will include things like bricks in a house (rectangles), keys on a computer keyboard (square) and bicycle wheels (circles). In the natural world, examples might include the pupils in the eye (circles) and the shape of many flowers (circles and triangles). What about things like the letter O in writing, the dots on a bar of music, or the zeros in a bank statement? These are often circles. It may not be possible to count the numbers of each shape, but try to estimate which is the most common. Why might circles have been chosen for the Olympic rings?

There isn't a precise answer to this question. In the physical world, rectangles are very common. They can fit together without gaps, like the bricks in a wall. Triangles are often used in buildings to give them strength. In the natural world, curved shapes such as circles are very common. In the world of media, the letter O and the number zero appear frequently. It is unlikely that anyone has attempted to count shapes to say which is the most common. Circles seem to be strong contenders, but you may have a different view. Shapes are important in everyday life. Different shapes are used for different reasons. Which shape is best for which purpose?

No parking

Draw examples of parallel, perpendicular, oblique and intersecting lines. Use a dictionary or the internet to look up the words. Do the descriptions match the drawings? Do changes need to be made? Look for lines in and around the school (e.g. a ladder) and think of what kind of lines they are. Compare answers with other people. Design a poster to show the difference between the different types of lines. Investigate how artists use lines to create illusions in their work (for example Franz Muller-Lyer).

Lines running side by side at an equal distance apart (equidistant) are called parallel lines. Small arrows can be used to show that two lines are parallel to each other. Real life examples of parallel lines include railway tracks and sleepers and double yellow lines. Parallel lines do not need to be the same length as each other. The most obvious example of a pair of parallel lines is the equals sign. Another good example can be found on a co-ordinate grid. Make a Möbius strip and investigate what kind of lines it has. What happens when it is cut in half along its length?

Post your thoughts

Collect some envelopes and place them face down. Look carefully at the folds and flaps, then mark all the angles that can be seen. Measure these angles with a protractor. What type of angles are they? Share ideas in a group and see if everyone agrees. Now look at more examples of envelopes and identify the angles. Are they different? Carefully open an envelope to form a net and examine how it has been constructed. Use this as a template for designing a new envelope. Look carefully at other packaging and try to spot the angles.

The back of an envelope usually contains lots of different types of angles, not just right angles. Usually there will be examples of acute angles, right angles, reflex angles and obtuse angles. Straight angles may also be found, though these are less obvious. A straight angle is an angle of 180 degrees. i.e. a straight line. A straight angle can change a direction to point in the opposite way. Are there any envelopes that only have 45 degree angles and right angles? Do some envelopes have right angles that split into more than one angle? Do some envelopes have straight angles that split into more than one angle?

5.7
Flag it up

Look at the flag design and discuss the different shapes. What difference do the shapes make to the lines of symmetry? Experiment with other shapes in the centre of the flag, and investigate whether these affect the line symmetry. Look in an atlas or on the internet and find the flags of the world. Are all flags rectangular? Do they all have some line symmetry? Design a new flag and challenge other people to work out its symmetrical properties.

This flag has two lines of reflective symmetry, one going vertically and one horizontally. A common mistake to make is to think of the flag as having four lines of symmetry, either because of the cross having four arms or the rectangle having four sides. The flag isn't symmetrical around the diagonal lines. The small circle, on its own, has an infinite number of lines of symmetry, but not when it is part of another shape. Are there flags with more than two lines of symmetry?

5.8
What a card!

Look carefully at a pack of playing cards and the designs used. Identify any familiar mathematical shapes. Now look at each card in turn and discuss their symmetrical properties. Use tracing paper to copy the cards and then rotate the cards under the paper to find out whether they have rotational symmetry or not. Have a go at designing a new set of cards, using other polygons for the suits. Is it possible to give them all rotational symmetry?

The faces of some playing cards do not have any rotational symmetry owing to the individual designs used. The Five of Diamonds has rotational symmetry of order two – the way it is and then turned round through 180 degrees. A common mistake is to think that the card has rotational symmetry of order four, but it is not symmetrical if it is rotated through 90 or 270 degrees. Another mistake is to think it has rotational symmetry of order one because it can only be turned round, or rotated, once. Are there any card designs that do have rotational symmetry of order four?

Try a practical investigation to solve this problem. Write a variety of words including OXO, MUM and NOON, on a piece of paper. Try rotating each word through 180 degrees. Does the word still look the same? Now try looking at the reflection of the word in a mirror. Does the word still look the same? Which words can be rotated or reflected and still look the same? Explore more words that can be rotated and reflected. Is it possible to predict which ones will look the same?

Some letters, such as M and T, look the same if they are reflected in a mirror but not if they are rotated. Some letters, such as S and Z, look the same if they are rotated but not if they are reflected in a mirror. Some letters, such as O and X, look the same if they are reflected in a mirror and if they are rotated. How the letters are put together in words determines whether the word will look the same if it is reflected or rotated. Where are reflection and rotation used in everyday life?

Predict which of the following shapes will tessellate: kite, oval, parallelogram, rhombus, triangle, pentagon, hexagon, circle, rectangle, semi-circle. Try joining them together and see what happens. Put the answers in a table. Share your ideas with another group. Do they have the same ideas? Think about real world examples of shapes that tessellate, such as bee honeycombs, and make a poster to illustrate tessellating shapes.

A tessellation is a repeating pattern made of identical flat shapes that cover a plane completely without overlapping. They fit snugly together without leaving gaps. Lots of people believe that regular pentagons will tessellate, but they don't. However some irregular pentagons can tessellate. Only three regular polygons tessellate: triangles, squares and hexagons. Can more unusual shapes tessellate? Explore the work of the Dutch graphic artist M. C. Escher to find some fascinating examples of tessellating shapes.

5.11
Dice dilemma

Two people sit back to back. One person has a solid shape or a diagram of a 3D shape to describe to the other. The other person draws the diagram without seeing the shape. The person drawing cannot ask questions. The person with the shape must give clear and correct instructions to help their partner. How many edges, faces and vertices does this shape have? Play this game with different 3D shapes. Points could be given to pairs that produce accurate pictures.

Each die is a cuboid or rectangular prism. A cuboid is a solid figure made up of six rectangular faces, 8 vertices and 12 edges. Two dice will have 24 edges. A common mistake when identifying the parts of a cuboid is to mix up the edges with faces. A face is the flat surface of a solid shape, and an edge is the line where two faces join. A vertex is a corner where several faces and edges come together. Sometimes dice have their sharp corners rounded to help them to roll more easily. One way to find the number of edges is Faces + Vertices = Edges + 2. Try it with some shapes to see if it always works. Are there other shapes which can make fair dice? How many faces, vertices and edges do they have?

5.12
Facing up to it

The tent is shaped like a triangular prism. Look closely at a triangular prism. You could make one using toothpicks and blu-tac. The number of faces can now be counted. What if you go inside the tent? How many faces will there be on the inside? How does a tepee differ from a tent? Collect different types of prisms and draw up a table to record the number of vertices, faces and edges of each.

The number of faces on a tent depends on what type of tent it is:
• a tetrahedron has 4 vertices, 6 edges and 4 faces
• a triangular prism has 6 vertices, 9 edges and 5 faces
• a square-based pyramid has 5 vertices, 8 edges and 5 faces

There are other types of tent, such as the pentagonal-based pyramid, hexagonal-based pyramid, octagonal-based pyramid and circular-based pyramid (or cone). The tent in the picture is a triangular prism, so it has 5 faces. Architects think about faces when designing buildings. Are there any buildings with a large number of faces?

Try drawing the different nets on a piece of paper, cut them out and fold them to find out which ones form boxes. Unfold boxes and look at their nets. Try to work out how the nets are chosen to minimise waste cardboard. Invent some more nets for other shapes and challenge other groups to work out whether they will fold to form a box. Remember to include some shapes that do not fold to make a box. Discuss why certain nets fold to make a 3D shape and others do not.

Net number 1 will fold to make a box in the shape of a triangular prism. None of the other nets will make a box. A net with three squares and two triangles can be arranged in several different ways. Three squares and one triangle will not make a box; neither will four squares and three triangles. What would be the difference between the nets for a triangular-based pyramid and a square-based pyramid? Try to visualise this before making the nets.

Mark out a 6 x 6 co-ordinate grid on squared paper. Mark all the different sets of co-ordinates on the grid, going along the bottom axis and then up the side axis for each pair of co-ordinates. Which pair of co-ordinates shows where the treasure is buried? Try designing a treasure map for another group to use. Playing games with co-ordinate grids, such as battleships, is a good way to become more familiar with co-ordinates.

The treasure is located at (3.5, 4.5). An easy mistake to make is to ignore the treasure's location between two lines on the map. It is important to read between the lines, and see the space halfway as being equivalent to .5 on both the x and y axes. Another common mistake is to read the x and y axes in the wrong order. For example, going up 3.5 and then along 4.5 and missing the treasure! Saying "along the corridor, up the stairs" is a useful reminder. Try making up other phrases to remember the order of co-ordinates.

5.15

Going plotty

Mark out a 6 x 6 co-ordinate grid on squared paper. Mark all the different sets of co-ordinates on the grid, going along the bottom axis and then up the side axis for each pair of co-ordinates. Which set of co-ordinates completes the square? Is it possible to have more than one set that completes the square? Invent more versions of this problem by moving the dots on the CD ROM version, or drawing a square on tracing paper, then marking two of the corners on a co-ordinate grid. Give the grid to a partner to find the missing corners.

In this problem there are three possible answers. All the squares are tilted which often causes confusion. It is not easy to recognise a square when it rests on one of its vertices. It may look like a diamond or a lozenge shape. The missing co-ordinates for making a small square are (2,0) and (3,3). The co-ordinates for making a larger square are (2,5) and (5,4), or (0,-1) and (3,-2). What if there were more negative numbers on the axes? Could other squares be made, or other shapes? What would be the co-ordinates for each shape?

5.16

Party challenge

Work in pairs to act out the instructions given in each of the speech bubbles. Which instruction results in a square? Alternatively, use a computer program such as Logo to investigate different commands. Try writing the commands for drawing two rectangles that join together, or a letter of the alphabet such as the letter T. Write some commands that involve different angles, such as a hexagon or a five-pointed star.

In this example a square is made by moving 3 paces forward, turning through 90 degrees, then repeating this movement three times. A common mistake is to repeat this four times because there are four sides to a square, or to turn by only 45 degrees. Different shapes require different angles and a different number of steps to form the sides. What shape is formed if the angles are 45 degrees? What happens if each side is a different number of steps?

5.1 Smile please

What do YOU think?

5.2 Try this

What do YOU think?

5.3 Check mate

What do YOU think?

5.4 Give us a ring

What do YOU think?

5.5 No parking

What do YOU think?

5.6 Post your thoughts

What do YOU think?

5.7 Flag it up

What do YOU think?

5.8 What a card!

What do YOU think?

5.9 Only OXO?

What do YOU think?

5.10 Tile it

What do YOU think?

5.11 Dice dilemma

What do YOU think?

5.12 Facing up to it

What do YOU think?

5.13 Nets

What do YOU think?

5.14 Buried treasure

What do YOU think?

5.15 Going plotty

What do YOU think?

5.16 Party challenge

What do YOU think?

6 Measures 1

Soon be time

Look at some pictures of clocks that only have hour hands. Practise reading the hour that they show. Now look at the minute hands. How does the minute hand help to break the hours down into smaller bits? Thinking about halves and quarters will help. Colour halves and quarters on a clock face. Try putting numbers round the clock for every minute. How many minutes are there in each quarter? Does everyone have the same ideas? Draw some clock pictures to make a school-day time diary.

The time can be read as three forty five, fifteen minutes to four or quarter to four. It is unusual to say 45 minutes past 3, but it is not wrong. A common mistake is to mix up the hour and minute hands and read the time as 20 past 9. Another error is to look at the hands and simply read the numbers that the hands are pointing to, for example, 9 minutes to 4 or 4 minutes past 9. Clocks can be confusing because the numbers that we see are the hours and we often have to work out the minutes for ourselves. Each time the minute hand moves to another number, 5 minutes have passed. So when a minute hand reaches 6 it is 30 minutes past the hour. Practising fractions and the five times table will make it easier to tell the time. What will the time be in another 30 minutes?

6.2
Just a minute

Create a number line from 0 to 24. Mark it in hours to represent a 24 hour clock. Where are a.m. and p.m.? Where would 11:59 a.m. be? What do you think comes after it? Does everyone agree? Look for different clocks, such as mobile phone, alarm, stopwatch, TV, oven, and so on. See what the clocks say for 11:59 a.m. and the number that follows. What do a.m. and p.m. stand for? What will 00:00 and 12:00 be called?

In one minute, the clock will show 12:00, which is 12:00 midday or 12:00 noon. This isn't either a.m. (ante meridiem) or p.m. (post meridiem), which mean 'before noon' and 'after noon'. Noon is exactly halfway through the day. Some digital clocks display this as 12:00 p.m. This can be confusing. Midnight is usually shown as 00:00, though some clocks might show this as 24:00. What will the time be one minute after midnight?

6.3
Clock it

Practise finding the time shown on an analogue clock. Normally we look for where the hour hand is first, but then often say the minutes first when we read out the time (e.g. 10 past 7). Now look at different times shown on a digital clock. The clock shows the hour first, and we normally say the hour first when we read out the time (e.g. 7:35). Set each type of clock for the same time and think about what the time is on each clock. Does everyone agree? Try adding 10 minutes to each time and reading out what the time will be.

Twenty to five means twenty minutes to five o'clock, or 4:40. Two of the clocks show this time, and all the other clocks are later. It is easy to mix up the hours and minutes, because with an analogue clock we often say the minutes first and then the hours, but with a digital clock we normally say the hours first and then the minutes. A common mistake is to confuse twenty to five with 5:20 or 5:40. What other mistakes might some people make when they read the time on a clock? Which times are the most confusing?

6.4
Cooking time

Use an analogue clock to practice counting on in hours and minutes. Then try it with a digital clock and see how the two types of clock compare. Is it possible to create a number line that helps people to count on in hours and minutes? Have a go at this, and see what other groups have done. Do different groups agree on the best way to create an hours and minutes number line? Now try some more cooking problems. For example, invent some weights for different foods and challenge another group to work out how long they need to cook.

The chicken needs to cook for 20 minutes for each 500 g. The chicken weighs 2.75 kg. First work out how many 500 g there are in the chicken. It might help to change the 2.75 kg to grams, which is 2750 g. Divide 2750 by 500, so $2750 \div 500 = 5\frac{1}{2}$. This means that there are $5\frac{1}{2}$ lots of 500 g in a 2.75 kg chicken. There are other ways to work this out. Each 500 g takes 20 minutes to cook so the whole chicken needs to cook for $5\frac{1}{2} \times 20$ mins, or 1 hour 50 minutes. If cooking starts at 11:35, then it should come out of the oven 1 hour 50 minutes later, which is 13:25. When would it come out of the oven if it goes in at 16:50? How long would it cook for it if weighs 4.2 kg?

In this example the time is written as a decimal. Make a table to convert decimal times to minutes, like the one opposite.

Find the film timetable for a local cinema or TV programmes and convert the running times they give into decimals. Try converting different length train journeys into decimal times.

Decimal time	Time in minutes
0.1 hour	6
0.2 hour	?
0.3 hour	?
0.4 hour	?
0.5 hour	
0.6 hour	
0.7 hour	
0.8 hour	
0.9 hour	

How long is 0.1 hour? What paper and pencil method would give the answer? Using a calculator, the sequence is 1 x 60 x 0.1, so 0.1 hour = 6 minutes. If the film is 3.1 hours long then it must last for 3 hours 6 minutes. A common mistake is to read 3.1 hours as 3 hours and 1 minute, or 3 hours and 10 minutes. How long would a film last if it was 3.7 hours long?

6.6
Search me

Use a place value table to practise adding days, hours and minutes. It will be like a hundreds, tens and units table, but there are 60 minutes in one hour, 24 hours in one day and 28, 29, 30 or 31 days in a month. Start by just adding minutes, then go on to minutes and hours, then finally try minutes, hours and days. Look online at real auction sites and see what timeframes are used. Invent some items to sell on an auction site and provide a starting and finishing time for another group to work out.

It might help to start by adding the minutes. 30 mins + 45 mins = 1 hr 15 mins. Then add the hours. 14 + 7 = 21 hours. Add the answers. 1hr 15 mins + 21 hrs = 22 hrs 15 mins. So the time will be 22:15. Now add the days. 29th April + 4 days = 3rd May. So the closing time for the auction is 22:15 on 03.05.07. It is more tricky if the hours come to a number greater than 24. This would move the date on another day. If the time remaining had been 4 days 9 hours and 45 minutes then the auction would have closed at 00:15 on 4th May. What would be the closing time if the time left was 6 days 11 hours 35 minutes?

6.7
Time zone

Use a place value table to practise adding days, hours and minutes. It will be like a tens and units table, but there are 60 minutes in one hour and 24 hours in one day. Start by just adding minutes, then go on to minutes and hours. Find out about time zones in different parts of the world. What is the time difference between the UK and New York? Is New York earlier or later? Invent some more flight departures and travel times, and see if another group can work out the arrival times.

Start by adding the travel time to the departure time. 08:15 + 7 hr 45 min = 16:00 hours. The time in New York is usually 5 hours earlier than the time in the UK. So, subtract 5 hours from 16:00, and the arrival time must be 11:00 on 6th August. It is easy to confuse times across time zones and to add or subtract hours in the wrong direction. Watch out for changes in the times in particular zones due to clocks being put forward or backwards. What would be the arrival time in Kuala Lumpur, if the flight takes 12 hrs 55 mins, and Kuala Lumpur is 8 hours ahead of the UK?

6.8
How fast?

Use the internet or a book to find out how to convert miles per hour to kilometres per hour and vice versa. Then convert Dave's speed to miles per hour, or Mel's speed to kilometres per hour. Is one of them going faster than the other? Try converting some common speed limits from miles per hour to kilometres per hour, or vice versa. Look up the speed of Formula 1 racing cars and challenge another group to convert them.

To compare the speeds, both of them need to be in the same units of measurement. One kilometre is approximately $\frac{5}{8}$ of a mile, so to convert 45 km/h to mph, multiply by 5 and divide by 8. Similarly, to convert 30 mph to km/h, multiply by 8 and divide by 5. In mph, Mel is going at 30 mph and Dave is going at about 28 mph. In km/h, Mel is going at about 48 km/h and Dave is going at 45 km/h. Whichever units are used, Mel is going faster. What would their speeds be if Mel was going $1\frac{1}{2}$ times as fast as Dave?

Use the internet or a conversion chart to find out about the relationship between mm, cm and metres. Practise converting measurements in metres (e.g. the height of people in the class) to cm and mm. Practise converting measurements in cm (e.g. the length of people's feet) to metres. Work out how many cm there are in a kilometre and how many mm there are in a kilometre. Think about these as fractions or multiples of each other. Explore lots of different measurements and convert them to different units.

A millimetre is $\frac{1}{1000}$ of a metre or 0.001 m. A centimetre is $\frac{1}{100}$ of a metre or 0.01 m. So a millimetre is ten times smaller than a centimetre. In other words a cm is ten times bigger than a mm. The correct answer is that a cm is 10 times a mm and $\frac{1}{100}$ of a metre. What fraction of a kilometre is a cm? In the different units of measurement, find out how far people come to school. How many journeys to school would it take to cover 1 thousand millimetres, centimetres or metres, or 10 thousand, or 1 million?

Put a 10 cm mark on the edge of a piece of card. Then use different colours to mark 20, 30, 40, 50 cm, etc along the same edge. Put a mark on the card for each of the measurements in the speech bubbles. Use the card to find things in the classroom that are about the same length as each of the measurements. Try estimating the size of small objects like books, people's feet, etc. Estimate the size of the handspans of people in the class. Find out whether two people in the class have the same handspan. Go on a handspan hunt around the school to find three things that are about the same length as a handspan.

A handspan is measured from the tip of the little finger to the tip of the thumb, when a person's hand is stretched out. A typical adult handspan is between 18 to 25 cm across. This is the same as 180 to 250 mm, or 0.18 to 0.25 m across. So the most likely speech bubble is that mum's handspan is about 200 mm. Try drawing hands with spans of 10 cm, 55 cm and 0.09 m. How does an adult's handspan compare with a child's? What would a baby's handspan be? Who might have the biggest handspan? Is there a relationship between handspan and length of arms or size of feet, etc? Predict and then find out.

6.11
Assembly time

Try estimating how many chairs will fit across the back of a classroom. Measure the chairs and the classroom wall and work it out using a paper and pencil method. Use a calculator to work out how many will fit. Use some squared paper to draw a plan of how many will fit. Finally put the chairs across the back of the room and count how many actually fit. Did all the methods give the same answer? Invent some more fitting furniture problems for another group to try.

It is easier to work out how many chairs fit if both measurements are in the same units. It may help to convert 8.5 m to cm by multiplying by 100, so 8.5 x 100 = 850 cm. Then divide this by the width of one chair, so 850 ÷ 54 = 15.74. It isn't possible to have a fraction of a chair, so the number of chairs that will fit is 15, not 16. In real life the calculation can be complicated by the shape of the legs and how the chairs fit together in a row. How many chairs would fit across the school hall? Do gaps need to be left? What difference will gaps make? How many chairs will fit in the hall and still leave space for people to get in and out?

6.12
Mind your head

Use the internet or a conversion chart to find out the relationship between feet and metres. Practise converting measurements in metres (e.g. the size of the classroom) to feet and inches. Practise converting measurements in feet and inches (e.g. the height of people in the class) to metres. Investigate the heights of different vehicles on the internet. Invent some height restriction problems for another group to try. What other situations are there where there is a height restriction?

It is easier to work out if the minibus will fit under the bridge if both measurements are in the same units. To find the height of the bridge we could convert 2.03 m to feet. We convert metres to feet by multiplying by 3.28, so 2.03 x 3.28 = 6.66 feet. To convert this to feet and inches multiply the .66 by 12, so .66 x 12 = 7.92 inches. Talk about why .66 needs to be multiplied by 12. This means that the height of the bridge is 6 feet and 7.92 inches. The minibus is 6 ft 9 in, which makes it too tall to go under the bridge. What height in metres would the bridge have to be for the minibus to fit through? Investigate vehicle heights and bridge heights on motorways and elsewhere. Are there bridges that some vehicles cannot get under?

Use the internet or a conversion chart to find out how to convert mph (miles per hour) to km/h (kilometres per hour) and km/h to mph. Try converting some common speed limits from mph to km/h, or vice versa. Then convert the car's speed to mph, or the speed of the bus to km/h. How far will they travel in one hour? How far will they travel in two hours? Create some more examples by choosing different speeds and travel times, and give these to another group to try.

In order to decide how quickly the car and bus are moving apart, their speeds need to be in the same units of measurement. One kilometre is approximately ⅝ of a mile, so to convert 80 km/h to mph, multiply by 5 and divide by 8. Similarly, to convert 40 mph to km/h, multiply by 8 and divide by 5. In mph, the car is travelling at about 50 mph. In km/h, the bus is travelling at about 64 km/h. The speed at which they are separating is 40 + 50 = 90 mph, or 80 + 64 = 144 km/h. So after two hours they will be 180 miles or 288 kilometres apart. How far apart would they be if the bus went twice as fast?

6.14
Offside

Find out more about what 24 m² means. Explore multiplying two numbers together to make a new number. How many ways can we make 24 by multiplying two numbers together? Knowing the factors of numbers makes it much easier to work out which numbers to multiply together. What happens with decimal numbers? Is it still possible to make 24 by multiplying two decimal numbers together? Choose a decimal number, such as 4.5, and use a calculator to work out what number to multiply it by to make 24.

It helps to know that m² means square metres not metres squared. 24 m² is the area of the carpet. Talk about which character has confused square metres and metres squared. Perimeter and area are also easily confused. Some people may think that the length of each side is 6 m, because 6 x 4 equals 24. Sides of this length would give the perimeter, not the area of the room. If a room has an area of 24 square metres then its sides could measure 1.5 m x 16 m. Would these be sensible dimensions? Are there more answers as well as this correct one? What are the possible side lengths for a playground with an area of 120 square metres?

6.15
Carpet cover

The amount of floor covered by the carpet depends on its area, not its perimeter. Use a textbook or the internet to look up how to find the area and how to find the perimeter of something. The textbook or internet will also indicate what units are used to measure area. Is it metres or square metres? Invent some carpets of different sizes and work out their areas and perimeters. Is it possible for the perimeter to increase when the area gets smaller, or for the area to increase when the perimeter gets smaller?

Perimeter and area are easily confused. The perimeter is the distance around the outside of the shape and is measured in length units, such as metres. The area is the amount of surface covered by the shape and is measured in square units, such as square metres. In this example the area of the carpet is 5 m x 5 m = 25 square metres. What is the difference between 25 square metres and 25 metres squared? How many metres squared is the carpet in the Concept Cartoon? What would the area be if each side of the carpet was 15 m long?

6.16
Totally tiled

To work out this problem it helps to get everything in the same units of measurement. The best unit for this problem will be centimetres. The tiles are 200 x 200 mm. What is that in centimetres? Use a book or the internet if necessary to convert the measurement. The wall is 3 x 2 m. What is that in centimetres? Use squared paper to draw the tiles in 1 square metre. How many tiles will fit? How many tiles will that be across the whole wall? Invent some more wall tiling problems for another group to try.

It helps to use the same unit of measurement for the wall and the tiles. The tiles are 200 x 200 mm, which is 20 x 20 cm, so the area of each tile is 400 sq cm. The wall is 2 x 3 m, which is 200 x 300 cm, so the area of the wall is 60 000 sq cm. The number of tiles that will fit is 60 000 ÷ 400 = 150 tiles. Another way to work this out is to find out how many tiles cover 1 square metre (25 tiles). There are 6 square metres of wall, which means that 25 x 6 tiles or 150 tiles are needed. How many tiles would fit in a wall 5 x 3 m?

Use a textbook or the internet to check how to find the area of a circle, if necessary. Try some simple calculations, such as finding the area of the circle when the radius is 4 m, 7 m, 10 m, 12 m, 16 m. Think about the difference between 100 square metres and 100 metres squared. Are they both the same size? How much will the weedkiller treat? Invent some weedkiller problems for another group to try.

The area of a circle is Π x radius squared. $\Pi = \frac{22}{7}$ or 3.14. In this example, this will be 3.14 x 16.5 x 16.5 = 855 sq m. Each box of weedkiller treats 100 sq m. So the number of boxes needed is 855 ÷ 100 = 8.55 boxes. This is more than 8 boxes, so 9 boxes must be needed. How many boxes would be needed if the lawn is 11.3 m radius? What would the perimeter of the lawn be?

Use a textbook or the internet to check how to find the area of a circle, if necessary. Try some simple calculations, such as finding the area of the circle when the radius is 4 m, 7 m, 10 m, 12 m, 16 m. Then try finding the area of an outer ring, where one of the circles is inside another. To do this, find the area of the bigger circle, then find the area of the smaller circle, then subtract the smaller area from the bigger area. Invent some bull's eye problems for another group to solve.

The area of a circle is Π x radius squared. The area of the path must be the area of the bigger circle minus the area of the smaller circle. In this example, the area of the path and the pond together is 3.14 x 7 x 7 = 3.14 x 49 sq m = about 154 sq m. The area of the pond is 3.14 x 6 x 6 = 3.14 x 36 sq m = about 113 sq m. This means that the path is 154 − 113 = 41 sq m. Another way to work this out is (3.14 x 49) − (3.14 x 36) = 3.14 x 13 = about 41 sq m. So they would need to buy 41 sq m of stone to cover the path. What would the area of the path be if the pond was 15 m diameter?

6.19
Birthday cake

Use a textbook or the internet to check how to find the perimeter of a circle, if necessary. Try some problems where the perimeter is important. For example, the wheels of Jane's bicycle have a diameter of 60 cm. How long are the tyres on her bicycle? How many times will she have to turn the wheels to get to the shops 5 km away? Invent some perimeter problems for another group to try.

The perimeter of a circle is ∏ x diameter of the circle. In this example, the length of ribbon needed is the perimeter of the circle round the cake, plus a little bit of overlap. This means that the ribbon needs to be 125.6 cm (3.14 x 40 cm) for the ends to touch, or about 127 cm to allow a little bit of overlap. How much ribbon would be needed if the cake was 55 cm diameter?

6.20
Chocolate boxes

Try modelling this with wooden cubes or squared paper. Put in one layer of boxes on the bottom of the crate and see how well they fit. Is there any space left over? Build up the layers until the top layer is filled. How many boxes fit in now? How much space is left altogether? Can any more boxes fit in the space that is left? Now invent your own chocolate box problems for another group to try.

The volume of the chocolate box is $18 \times 5 \times 12 = 1080$ cm³. The volume of the packing crate is $60 \times 60 \times 60 = 216\,000$ cm³. So 200 boxes ($216\,000 \div 1080$) should fit in the crate. But it isn't as simple as this. The shape of the boxes means that not all the space in the crate can be used. The boxes don't stack exactly to use all the space. The most that will fit in the crate is 198 boxes. Is there an ideal box shape to use all of the space in the packing crate? How many would fit if the crate was twice as big?

6.1 Soon be time

What do YOU think?

6.2 Just a minute

What do YOU think?

6.3 Clock it

What do YOU think?

6.4 Cooking time

What do YOU think?

6.5 Watching time

What do YOU think?

6.6 Search me

What do YOU think?

6.7 Time zone

What do YOU think?

6.8 How fast?

What do YOU think?

6.9 Metric musings

What do YOU think?

6.10 Hand it to me

What do YOU think?

6.11 Assembly time

What do YOU think?

6.12 Mind your head

What do YOU think?

6.13 Separate ways

What do YOU think?

6.14 Offside

What do YOU think?

6.15 Carpet cover

What do YOU think?

6.16 Totally tiled

What do YOU think?

6.17 Weedkiller

What do YOU think?

6.18 Pond dipping

What do YOU think?

6.19 Birthday cake

What do YOU think?

6.20 Chocolate boxes

What do YOU think?

Measures 2

Do all teaspoons hold the same amount? Estimate how much a teaspoon might hold using wooden or plastic centimetre cubes. One cubic centimetre is the same volume as one millilitre. Try different numbers of cubes and see which looks like roughly the same amount as a teaspoon full of liquid. Collect some teaspoons and fill them with water. Measure how much they hold. Do they hold the same amount? How many teaspoons will a teacup hold?

One cubic centimetre is the same volume as one millilitre. It takes a block of 2000 cubes to make 2 L or 2000 millilitres. We would need a block of 50 cubes to make 50 ml. 30 ml would be the same as a block of 30 cubes. A block of 5 cubes would make 5 ml. The block of 5 cubes is closest to a teaspoon. A teaspoon normally holds about 5 ml. Liquid medicine is usually measured in 5 ml amounts. How much do a dessertspoon and a tablespoon hold? Choose different numbers of cubes, and then try to guess which containers would hold them. How close are the estimates?

Use the internet or a conversion chart to find out about millilitres and litres. Work out how many millilitres there are in a litre. Then it should be possible to find out how many times 250 ml will fit into 2 litres, or how many times two litres will fill 250 ml. How many 5 ml teaspoons will fit into 250 ml? How many will fit into 2 litres? Invent some more water bottle problems for another group to try.

To compare the different containers, it helps if the units of measurement are the same. Two litres convert to 2000 ml. How many lots of 250 ml are there in 2000 ml? Either add lots of 250 millilitres together to get to 2000 ml or divide 2000 by 250 (2000 ÷ 250 = 8). This means that the 250 ml bottle will fill the 2 L container exactly 8 times. How many 250 ml bottles would fill an 8 litre container? Collect different sized bottles. Estimate how much liquid would fill them. How many of the small containers would fill the larger ones or how many small bottles will the large ones fill? Try comparing litre containers with pint and gallon containers.

7.3
Paint it

Think about what 250 ml and 500 ml would be in litres or what 1.5 L and 2.5 L would be in millilitres. Then it should be possible to investigate which cans are needed to make up 2.5 L. Try using containers of water to work it out. Is there more than one possible answer? Find out what size of cans paint is usually sold in, then invent some more paint can problems for another group to try.

To work out which paint cans are needed, it helps if the units of measurement are the same. 1000 millilitres equals one litre. The medium can holds 500 ml which is half a litre (0.5 L). The small can holds 250 ml which is a quarter of a litre (0.25 L). The big can holds one and a half litres (1.5 L).

It is now easier to see that one small can is not enough. A quarter of a litre (0.25 L) is much less than two and a half litres (2.5 L). One way to make exactly 2.5 L is to have two half litre (0.5 L) medium sized cans and six quarter litre (0.25 L) small cans. Which other groups of cans could be used to make 2.5 L? What if paint is more expensive in small cans? Would this be the best way to buy the paint? Which cans could be used to make 4.5 L?

7.4
What a gas

Use the internet or a conversion chart to find out about gallons and litres. How many litres are there in 1 gallon? How many gallons are there in 1 litre? Use the internet or a car magazine to find out how big the petrol tank is on some popular cars. How much do they hold in gallons and in litres? How much would it cost to fill the tank? What are the approximate dimensions of the tank?

To compare the different amounts of petrol, it helps if the units of measurement are the same. 4.546 litres (or 4.5 litres approximately) is equivalent to 1 gallon. This means that 45 litres is a little bit less than 10 gallons. Another way to work this out is to say 1 litre is equivalent to 0.22 gallons, so 45 litres equal 9.9 gallons (45 x 0.22). In many popular cars 45 litres will be about a tank full.

We can also work out 45 litres as pints. 1 litre is equivalent to 1.76 pints, so 45 litres equals 79.2 pints (1.76 x 45). 79.2 pints are equivalent to 9.9 gallons. How does this compare with how much water it takes to fill a bath or how much liquid people normally drink in a year?

Feeling flushed

Use the internet or a conversion chart to find out about millilitres, centilitres and litres. Practise converting measurements in litres (for example the amount of liquid in a large container of milk) to cl and ml. Practise converting measurements in cl or ml (for example the amount of toothpaste in a tube or cough medicine in a bottle) to litres. Investigate how much water we use at home doing things like brushing teeth, flushing the toilet, and having a shower or bath.

To compare the different amounts, it helps if the units of measurement are the same. There are 10 millilitres in a centilitre and 100 centilitres in a litre. So 8 litres equals 800 centilitres, or 8000 millilitres. This is approximately the amount used when a toilet is flushed. How much water would this be for a family of four people, if each person flushes the toilet 4 times a day on average? What household tasks would use 80 litres, 80 centilitres or 80 millilitres of water?

Water shortage

Try to estimate how much water is used by one person, on average, every day. Think about what water is used for. Would the amount of water be the same if the people were at home rather than camping? Is the amount of water used the same in every country in the world? Use the internet to find out more about the amount of water used. Remember there are five people. If a rain barrel collects about 100 000 litres of water during the year, would that be enough water for five people?

Water consumption varies greatly. The average water consumption in this country is about 150 litres per person per day. This includes drinking, washing, cooking, etc. This would mean that the water in the tank would last a little more than a day. The amount of water used would be lower if they were camping. In some countries water consumption is as low as 10 litres per day, or even less. The water in the tank would then last about 19 days. How long would the water last if the tank holds 1350 L of water? Of course in real life the water tank may be filled up again! What is the minimum amount of water to meet a human's needs? How long could you survive if it doesn't rain and you only have water from the water tank? How would you make the water last as long as possible?

7.7
Something fishy

It's important to be able to identify numbers on number lines. Put a pencil mark anywhere on a 1 − 100 number line and try reading off the number. Try this with other number lines, such as 1 − 1000 and 0.1 − 1.0. Discuss what the gaps or intervals between the numbers will be. Try this with a circular number line and see whether the numbers change at all. Practise reading scales using different thermometers, measuring cylinders and spring balances. Then invent an interesting scale-reading problem for another group to solve.

It's easy to make a mistake and not read the scale properly. The scale shows kg not g. The pointer is pointing between 0.7 and 0.8. Half way between the two numbers is 0.75 kg. It might help to convert from kilograms to grams to check who is right. I kilogram equals 1000 grams, so 0.75 kg is 0.75 x 1000 = 750 g.

Here is another way to work it out. There are ten divisions on the scale so each division is 1000 g ÷ 10 = 100 g. The pointer is between 0.7 and 0.8 kilograms on the scale, so the fish must be between 700 and 800 grams. Halfway between the two divisions is 750. So the fish must be 750 grams. Where would the pointer be if the scales went up to 4 kg?

7.8
Water weigh

Investigate weighing different amounts of water, using something like a measuring cylinder to measure the volume. What is the relationship between the weight and the volume of water? How much does 100 ml of water weigh? How much does 1 litre of water weigh? Try it with other liquids, such as fruit juice. Try filling different size containers with water and estimating their weight, then checking the answer. Use the internet to find out the difference between mass and weight. Invent some more water container problems for another group to try.

One cubic centimetre, filled with water, contains exactly one millilitre and the water weighs one gram. One litre of water contains 1000 millilitres, so it weighs 1000 grams, or one kilogram. This means that a 40 litre container will weigh 40 kg. To be more precise, it is the mass of water that we are measuring, not the weight. Water is heavy and carrying it for long distances is not easy. Think about what this means for women and children who carry buckets of up to 20 litres of water on their heads for several kilometres in many countries. Fill up some bottles to see what it feels like. What would the container weigh if it holds 185 litres of water?

Start by converting the amount of food into the same units of measurement. Use a book or the internet if, necessary, to check how to convert kilograms to grams. How much food will the guinea pig eat in 5 days? How much will it eat in 10 days? When will the food run out? Think about other situations where something is being used up, such as how long a packet of breakfast cereal will last. Invent some similar problems for another group to solve.

To work out how long the food will last, it helps if the units of measurement are the same. To convert kilograms to grams, multiply by 1000. So the bag of food is 1.5 x 1000 = 1500 grams. To find out how long the food will last, divide the amount of food by the amount that the guinea pig eats each day. 1500 ÷ 30 = 50 days. Common mistakes include ignoring the decimal point in 1.5, reading 1.5 kg as 1050 g, and reading 1.5 kg as 1005 g. How long would the bag last if it is a 7 kg bag? How long would this bag last if the guinea pig eats only 23 grams each day?

It might help to convert the amounts into the same units of measurement. Use a book or the internet, if necessary, to check how to convert kilograms to grams. What has to happen to make the scales balance? Should the numbers be added or subtracted? Choose a range of common objects, such as a watch, a book or a bottle of water, and estimate what the scales will read, in either grams or kilograms. Invent some scale balancing problems for another group to try.

To work out how to make the scales balance, it helps if units of measurement are the same. To convert kilograms to grams, multiply by 1000. So 0.025 kg equals 25 grams (0.025 x 1000). If there is 95 g on one side of the scales and 25 g on the other, the amount needed to balance the scales is 95 − 25 = 70 g. This can also be written as 0.07 kg. Common mistakes are to read 0.025 kg as 0.025 g, 2.5 g or 250 g. What needs to be added to make the scales balance if the apple weighs 48 g? What if there is a bag of apples weighing 205 g?

7.11
I'm bigger than you

Measure an angle of 45 degrees and draw lines of 5 cm to make the angle. Now draw another angle of 45 degrees and draw lines of 10 cm to make the angle. Next, measure an angle of 45 degrees and draw lines of 15 cm to make the angle. Measure the three angles again. What do you notice about the angles? What kinds of mistakes might people make in drawing angles? Create a poster to help people to avoid making angle mistakes.

A common mistake is to think that the size of an angle depends on the length of the lines that make the angle. Another common mistake is to think that the size of an angle depends on the size of the arc across the angle, or on the area enclosed by the angle and the arc. In fact none of these makes any difference to the size of the angle. It is the amount that one line has turned away from the other line that tells us the size of the angle, not the lengths of the lines or the arc. Compare angles made by opening doors, books, windows, etc.

7.12
About time

Think about how many degrees there are in 12 hours, a complete circle round the clock. How many degrees will there be in 6 hours, half of the circle? How many will there be in 3 hours? How many will there be in 1 hour? Now it should be possible to work out the angle between the two hands. Try some more clock faces with different times and work out the angle between the hands. Work out how fast the hands travel, in degrees per minute or degrees per hour. Invent some more clock face problems for another group to try.

There are 360 degrees in the 12 hours round the whole clock face. So when the hour hand moves one hour it turns through 30 degrees (360 ÷ 12). You turn through 5 hour spaces on the clock to go from 6 to 11, so the angle between them must be 150 degrees (5 x 30). It is also possible to read the angle by starting at 11 and moving clockwise round to 6. Now the angle is 210 degrees (7 x 30). What will the precise angle be if we work out how much the hour hand has moved? What are the two possible angles when the clock reads 10 past one?

Think about how many degrees there are in a complete circle round the compass. How many degrees will there be going from north to south, halfway round the compass? How many will there be going from north to east? North to north east? North to north north east? Create a table to show all the different compass points and their directions in degrees from north. Now invent some compass direction problems for another group to solve.

There are 360° in the complete circle around the compass. North has a compass direction of 0°, east is 90° clockwise from north, south is 180° clockwise (or anticlockwise) from north, and west is 270° clockwise from north. NE, SE, SW and NW are midway between these points. These directions can be divided again, into NNE, ENE, and so on. Somebody facing NNE has turned through 22.5° **clockwise** from north. If the person then turned 157.5° **clockwise**, they would be facing 22.5 + 157.5 = 180° from north, which is south. Turning 157.5° **anti-clockwise** means they would be facing SW (that is, a 22.5° turn to face N, then another 135° to turn from N to SW). What direction would they be facing if they turned 315° clockwise?

Use books or the internet to check exactly what shape a quadrilateral is. Does it include a rectangle? A square? A rhombus? A kite? A trapezium? A parallelogram? Try drawing each of these and look carefully at the diagonals. Is the relationship between the side length and the diagonal length always the same? Is there a pattern? Create a poster to explain to others what the pattern is.

A common mistake is to think of only one type of quadrilateral, such as a rectangle. In any rectangle the diagonals are always longer than the sides, and the same length as each other. It doesn't matter what shape the rectangle is – the sides are always shorter than the diagonals. However quadrilaterals can be lots of different shapes as well as rectangles. For example, think about a kite shape. In a kite one of the diagonals could be the same length as two of the sides and shorter than the other two, or shorter than all of the sides. Is there a quadrilateral where both diagonals are shorter than the sides?

7.15
Swap shop

Understanding currency exchange rates is like understanding how to convert one unit of measurement into another, such as gallons to litres. Use the internet to find the exchange rate for £1 in different currencies, such as Indian rupees, Swedish kroner, and so on. Carry out a survey of all the different currencies that people in the class have used, and what their exchange rates are. Use the internet to find out about commission and who gets paid commission for the work that they do.

An easy mistake is to do the conversion the wrong way round, and say €1 = £1.46. In this example the exchange rate is £1 = €1.46, so €250 will cost £171.23 (250 ÷ 1.46).

Another easy mistake to make is to forget to include the commission or to read the 1.5% as £1.50. If the commission is 1.5% of £171.23, this means it costs another £2.57 to buy the euros (£171.23 × 1.5% = £2.57). So the total cost of buying the euros is £171.23 + £2.57 = £173.80. What would €250 cost if the exchange rate is £1 = €1.36 and the commission is 2.5%? What would be an easy way to check the approximate price of something in euros if exchange rate was £1 = €1.46?

7.16
Sink or swim

Look at examples of maps and find out what scale is used. For example, a map might be 1 cm to 1 km, that is 1:100 000 (cm). Think about what this means in real life. Measure a piece of A4 paper in cm, and try drawing a 1:10 scale drawing of the paper. Measure one of the desks in the classroom in cm, and try a 1:10 scale drawing. Then measure the classroom and try a 1:100 scale drawing. Look at different magnifications on electronic maps and work out what the scale is for each.

A scale drawing does not change the shape of something, only its size. The swimming pool is reduced to 1/200 of its actual size. It may be easier to work out what that means if the dimensions are converted to centimetres. If the pool is 9 m by 15 m, then that can be written as 900 by 1500 cm. On a 1/200 scale drawing one side will be 900/200 = 4.5 cm, and the other side will be 1500/200 = 7.5 cm. This can also be written as 45 mm by 75 mm. A quick way to work it out is to divide the actual size by 2. The answer will be in cm. What would be a quick way to work out the actual size of something from the drawing? What size would the pool be on the drawing if the scale changed to 1:50? What would be a quick way to work this out?

7.1 Tea time

What do YOU think?

7.2 Filling up

What do YOU think?

7.3 Paint it

What do YOU think?

7.4 What a gas

What do YOU think?

7.5 Feeling flushed

What do YOU think?

7.6 Water shortage

What do YOU think?

7.7 Something fishy

What do YOU think?

7.8 Water weigh

What do YOU think?

7.9 Feeding time

What do YOU think?

7.10 Weighing things up

What do YOU think?

7.11 I'm bigger than you

What do YOU think?

On an analogue clock the angle between the hands will be 100 degrees

I think it will be 150 degrees

I think it will be 165 degrees

I think it will be 195 degrees

7.12 About time

What do YOU think?

7.13 Which way

What do YOU think?

7.14 Doubtful diagonals

What do YOU think?

What do YOU think?

7.16 Sink or swim

What do YOU think?

 Data **Handling**

Pizza pictures

Find examples of pictographs in books, newspapers or on the internet. Look at how pictures or symbols can be used to represent numbers of people. In this pictograph, what does one pizza represent? What about ¼ of a pizza? Work through the table to put in the numbers of children choosing each type of pizza. How many choose cheese and tomato? What would the pictograph look like if it was for a whole school? Invent some more pizza problems for another group to try.

Pictographs use symbols or pictures to represent numbers. In this example, pictures of pizzas are used to represent children, with each pizza representing 4 children. 3½ pizzas means that 14 children (3½ x 4) chose cheese and tomato pizza. A common mistake is to ignore the key and count one whole pizza as one child. How many children like BBQ chicken? How many children were surveyed altogether?

8.2
Where to start?

Look at some examples of graphs in books or on the internet. Find out whether there is any obvious pattern in the numbers used at the start of the vertical scale. Are there examples that start at any number other than zero? Would the graph look any different? Would the meaning of the graph be different? What about the horizontal scale? Are numbers always used on each scale?

A common mistake is to start labelling the vertical scale at one. In most graphs the vertical scale starts at zero. In this graph it is not clear if there were any people who could get to school in less than five minutes. It would be helpful to start both axes at zero. It is possible to start with another number. If the graph was for pulse rates after a race, starting at zero on the horizontal axis might not be a good idea. Everyone will have a pulse rate much higher than this! Starting at zero would make it difficult to fit other pulse rates on the graph using a sensible scale. Which sorts of data might start with zero and which might not? Collect some data and try it out.

8.3
What sort?

Use books or the internet to find out what types of charts, graphs or tables can be used to display data. Are there some that are good for every type of data? Are some better for certain kinds of data, and other types better for other kinds of data? Draw up a table to show the advantages and disadvantages of different ways of displaying data and find some examples of each in newspapers and magazines.

Pie charts are a popular way to display data because they are quite easy to use and because they are very visual in the way that they show proportions. There are computer programs that can help to construct them. However, a pie chart isn't always the best way of displaying data. If there are lots of small slices in the pie chart then it can be difficult to understand. If the size of each slice is very similar then it may not be easy to see what each slice is worth. In this example the best type of chart to use will depend on the number of categories in the data. What would be the best way to display how much it rains each day during a month?

8.4
Number sort

Start with the set of whole numbers from 1 - 21, and explore how many different ways they could be sorted into groups of similar types of numbers. Some possible ways of sorting numbers include negative, positive, odd, even, prime, non-prime, square, cube, triangular and numbers with more than two factors. Which numbers go in which set? Do some belong to more than one set? Think about how the results could best be displayed. Some possibilities are tables, tree diagrams, Carroll diagrams and Venn diagrams. What are the advantages of each method of displaying the results?

There are lots of different ways of classifying numbers. However, not all of them will be useful with any particular set of numbers. In this example, there are no negative numbers, or square or cube numbers, except the number one, so these ways of grouping are not very useful. The set of numbers does contain prime, non-prime and triangular numbers, so these methods of grouping could be useful. Were there any other ways of grouping? Did anyone think about Fibonacci numbers? Would the method of grouping change if all the numbers between 10 and 30 were added to the list?

It isn't possible to look up the answer to this problem in a book or on the internet. Working systematically through different possibilities is helpful. For example, see if any of the rows or columns could be 'divides by 2', 'divides by 3, by 4, by 5, by 6', and so on. Then look for types of numbers, such as square, cube, prime, triangular, and so on. Is there any obvious pattern in the Carroll diagram? Invent some more Carroll diagrams with missing labels for another group to try.

The Carroll diagram is a sorting table named after Lewis Carroll, the famous author. It is a rectangular grid that organises data into groups or sets. The two rows will have a yes/no answer – that is, things can go in one row or the other, but not both. The same is true for the two columns. In this example, the labels for the columns could be 'even' and 'not even' numbers. The labels for the rows could be 'divides by 9' and 'doesn't divide by 9'. Depending on what numbers are chosen, there might be more than one way to complete the Carroll diagram. Are there any other possibilities in this example? Could different numbers work with the same headings?

It isn't possible to look up the answer to this problem in a book or on the internet. Working systematically through different possibilities is helpful. For example, see if any of the circles could be 'divides by 2', 'divides by 3, by 4, by 5, by 6', and so on. Then look for types of numbers such as square, cube, prime, triangular, and so on. Is there any obvious pattern in the Venn diagram? Invent some more Venn diagrams with missing labels for another group to try. Find out what a Venn diagram with three circles might look like.

Each circle in a Venn diagram represents a particular type or group of numbers. Outside the circles are things that are not in either of those groups. Where the circles overlap (intersect) we put things that fit into both groups. In this example, the labels for the circles could be 'even' and 'square' numbers. In the space where the circles overlap (the intersection) are numbers that are both 'even' and 'square'. Outside the circle are numbers that are 'not even' and are 'not square'. Where would 16, 20, 25, 40, 45 and 49 go in the Venn diagram? What if the labels were changed to composite and square numbers? What if there was a third circle labelled prime numbers?

8.7
Missing

Look up how to draw Venn diagrams. Find out what goes into the place where the circles overlap (the intersection). Think what might go into the rectangle round the circles. It might help to make the Venn diagram using plastic hoops and number cards from 1 - 25. Put the numbers into the hoops. Then look again at this example and decide whether all the numbers are in the right place and whether there might be any numbers missing or in the wrong place. Draw some Venn diagrams with some numbers missing or in the wrong place, and see if another group can spot the problem.

A Venn diagram is a picture that shows two or more sets. Things that belong in a set are put in a circle. Often Venn diagrams have overlapping circles. The numbers in the middle belong to both sets. In this example only 15 belongs in both sets. A rectangle is sometimes drawn round a Venn diagram. This contains all of the numbers. We call this the universal set. In this example the universal set includes all the numbers from 1 - 25. They all have to be inside the rectangle. If they do not belong in the circles they have to go in the space around the circles. In this example there are numbers missing from the rectangle. The missing numbers are 1, 2, 4, 7, 8, 11, 13, 14, 16, 17, 19, 22 and 23. None of these go in the circles because they are not in the three or five times tables. What would the Venn diagram look like if it shows numbers from 1 - 50 or the labels were changed?

8.8
Open to interpretation

Use the bar chart to find out how many of the people use each different way of travelling to work. Which seems to be most popular? Which seems to be least popular? Discuss how the information might have been collected. Which people might have been asked? Where might they have been asked? When might they have been asked? Could the answer to any of these questions make a difference to the numbers? Use the internet to look for examples of graphs or charts that might be misleading.

In this example the bar chart appears to show that the most popular way of travelling to work is by car. However we don't have enough information to be certain. How people travel to work might depend on who was surveyed (e.g. if people were surveyed in a car park then they may be more likely to prefer travelling by car). It could also depend on what time of day it is, or what time of year (e.g. far more people might walk or cycle in good weather). So really all the answers could be correct. What might the bar chart look like if people were surveyed in a bus station?

Draw a scattergraph to see what relationship there is, if any, between finger length and mental maths scores. Discuss what the results appear to show. Think about what might cause these results. Might there be something that is missing from the table? If so, what could it be? If there could be something else, draw two separate graphs to show the possible relationship between finger length or mental maths scores against this other thing.

The table seems to show that people with longer index fingers are better at mental maths. If the data comes from a small sample of people, then the results might just be a coincidence. It is possible that both columns are related to something esle, such as age. A 16 year old will usually have longer fingers and be better at mental maths than a 6 year old. However, researchers did find a relationship between the difference in the length of the index and ring fingers and scores on maths and literacy tests. How could we explain a table that seems to show that the number of pensioners in a town seems to be related to the number of skateboard parks?

∞

8.10
Divide the pie

Explore some simple examples of pie charts. Using slices of pizza is easy to follow. How is the size of each slice calculated if 3 people each have a slice? What about 6 people? 10 people? 24 people? 50 people? Look this up in a book or on the internet if necessary. If there are 24 slices and one person gets 3 slices, how big a piece is that? How big a piece is 5 slices? 11 slices? Choose something to survey, such as favourite pop stars or how people travel to school, and draw a pie chart to display the data.

A pie chart looks like a pie or a pizza cut into slices. In this example each slice will represent the number of readers who read a particular newspaper. If most of the people read one of the papers, its slice will be very big. To get the size of the slices we need to work out how much of the circle to use for each one. There are 90 readers altogether. They will fill the whole circle (or eat the whole pie!). To turn through a complete circle we rotate $360°$. So to work out each reader's slice we divide $360°$ by $90 = 4°$. If 20 people read the Natterer then this is $20 \times 4° = 80°$. If 45 people read the Gas then this is $45 \times 4° = 180°$. What will be the size of the slice if the Natterer's readership drops to 5 people?

8.11

Going steady

Try drawing some graphs of everyday events. Here are some examples:
* the distance a car travels on a road if it goes at 30 mph
* the temperature inside an oven when it is turned on to bake some potatoes
* the height of an adult during a year
* the number of cars passing a school over 24 hours

Draw some graphs for another group and see how many possible ways they can explain what each graph shows.

When a bath is being steadily filled with water, the volume will also increase steadily. The graph that shows this is graph A. A common mistake is to think that it is graph B, because the water in the bath looks like it levels off. Graph C is interesting because it could be correct if we were measuring the amount of water going into the bath, but not if it is the total volume of water in the bath. This graph shows how important it is to label the axes clearly. What would the graph be like if the tap was left running and the bath overflowed? What would it look like if someone suddenly made the water run faster or kept turning the tap on and off? Would the graph change when the person gets into and out of the bath?

8.12

Through the roof

Try creating some graphs of common events. Some useful examples are:
* the temperature of a sitting room after someone goes to bed at night
* how the size of a baby changes as it grows into an adult
* how the size of a baby crab changes as it grows into an adult crab
* the amount of day length over a year

Draw some graphs for another group and see how many possible ways they can explain what the graph shows.

If house prices are rising steadily, the level of the graph will increase steadily. If they are rising less each month, then the graph will still show an increase but will gradually go flatter. This gives a curved graph not a straight line. The graph that shows this is graph B. A common mistake is to think that it is graph A, because the level keeps on going up. If the house prices were increasing the same amount each month then graph A could be correct. Another mistake is to think that it is graph D, because the line goes down. This graph would mean that house prices are falling faster each month rather than increasing. How will the graph change if house prices go down quickly and then gradually recover?

Have a look at some mileage charts in atlases. Measure the distance between two towns that are fairly close together, then check the distance on the mileage chart. Find out how to read down and across to get the correct distance. Look up how to do this if necessary. Try some more distances and get more confident in reading the mileage chart. Think about what mistakes people are likely to make in reading the chart, and produce a poster to explain how to read the chart correctly.

A mileage chart is a convenient way of showing the distances between several different places. The way to read the table is to read down from one town until level with the other town. That figure is the mileage between the two places. None of the figures need to be added up – the distance is the single figure in the table. So the distance between Nottingham and Cambridge is 89 miles. What is the distance between Norwich and York?

∞

Modes are easily confused with other terms, including mean, median, average and range of values. Look up definitions of the mode, mean, median, average and range. See how these apply to the list of shoe sizes. Draw a bar chart of the shoe sizes and see if it is possible to identify the mode from the chart.

There are three types of averages: mode, median and mean. The mean is what most people mean when they say 'average'. The mode is the number or object that occurs most often in a set of data. If no value occurs more than once then there isn't a mode. In this example there are two modes because shoe sizes 2 and 8 occur the most often. Knowing the mode is important in real life. In this example, it is important to manufacture more of the most popular shoes, otherwise there would not be enough of the popular sizes and too many of the unpopular sizes. What are the mean, the median and the range of the shoe sizes? See if is possible to work out a set of 5 numbers, if the mode is 6, the mean is 12 and the median is 15. What are the numbers?

8.15

Pick me

Look at the winning numbers for the last 20 weeks of the lottery. Find out whether certain numbers have come up more often than others. Have certain types of numbers come up more often than others (e.g. prime numbers, square numbers)? Do certain numbers seem to be lucky? Talk about whether numbers that have proved lucky in the past will still be lucky in the future, and whether people would have a better chance of winning by choosing these numbers.

A common mistake is to think that certain numbers have a better chance of winning the lottery than other numbers. In fact any six numbers are as likely to occur in a fair lottery as any six others. However, just because all numbers have an equal chance of being drawn, it doesn't mean that they are actually drawn out the same number of times. Some numbers are drawn out more often than others, just by chance. The chance of winning the lottery, when six balls are drawn, is approximately fourteen million to one. Some numbers seem more popular with people who do the lottery than others (e.g the numbers 1 - 12, multiples of 7, and numbers less than 32). Why might some numbers be more popular than others?

8.16

Play your cards right

Make up a small pack of 20 cards, consisting of the Ace, King, Queen, Jack and the ten of all four suits. Now the numbers are easy to work with. What is the probability of selecting an Ace from this pack? What about the Queen of Spades? A red card? Any King? Any King or Queen? Any card except a 10? What is the probability of selecting each of these from the full pack of cards? Make up some playing card probability problems for another group to try.

The probability of drawing a Spade from a deck of cards is 13 in 52, as there are 13 Spades in a pack of 52 playing cards. This can be simplified to $\frac{1}{4}$. If the Ace of Spades has already been drawn out, then there are only 12 Spades left in the next 51 cards. So the probability of the next card being a Spade is $\frac{12}{51}$. If the Ace of Spades is put back in the pack and the pack is shuffled, the probability of the next card being a Spade is now $\frac{13}{52}$, or $\frac{1}{4}$. What is the probability of the Ace of Spades being drawn again as the next card?

8.1 Pizza pictures

What do YOU think?

8.2 Where to start?

What do YOU think?

8.3 What sort?

What do YOU think?

I would put the positive numbers in one group and all the negative numbers in another

I would group these numbers as primes and non-primes

11, 2, 6, 10, 7, 14, 1, 3, 5, 15, 1, 13, 21

I would group the numbers as square and cube numbers

I would put all the triangular numbers together

8.4 Number sort

What do YOU think?

I can't think of any headings for this Carroll diagram

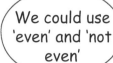

We could use 'even' and 'not even'

	70, 14, 120	77, 21, 49
	54, 108, 18	63, 27, 171

We could put 'prime numbers' and 'not prime numbers' on one side

One side could be 'divides by 7' and 'doesn't divide by 7'

8.5 What's my label?

What do YOU think?

8.6 What am I ?

What do YOU think?

8.7 Missing

What do YOU think?

8.8 Open to interpretation

What do YOU think?

This table shows that people with longer index fingers are better at maths

I think it means that people with smaller fingers don't like maths

Finger Length (cm)	Mental maths scores
5	15
5.5	20
6	16
6.5	19
7	18
7.5	20
8	21
8.5	23
9	19
9.5	28
10	29

I think it might be a coincidence

I think it might be that people with the higher maths scores are older

8.9 Missing link

What do YOU think?

To work out each section of the pie chart you divide 90 by the number of readers of a newspaper then × 360°

I'd say divide the number of people by 360°

I think you divide 360° by the number of readers

Use this information to draw a pie chart

Newspaper	Number of readers
The Daily Blab	15
The Gas	45
The Chin-Wag	10
The Natterer	20
Total	90

I'd say divide 360° by 90 then multiply by the number of readers

8.10 Divide the pie

What do YOU think?

8.11 Going steady

What do YOU think?

8.12 Through the roof

What do YOU think?

8.13 Between places

What do YOU think?

8.14 Popular shoes

What do YOU think?

8.15 Pick me

What do YOU think?

8.16 Play your cards right

What do YOU think?

References

- Alexander R. (2006) Towards dialogic teaching. York: Dialogos.

- Black P. and Wiliam D. (1998) Inside the black box. Kings College, London.

- Black P., Harrison C., Lee C., Marshall B. and Wiliam D. (2002) Working inside the black box. Kings College, London.

- Hodgen J. and Wiliam D. (2006) Mathematics inside the black box. London: Nfer Nelson.

- Keogh B. and Naylor S. (1999) Concept Cartoons, teaching and learning in science: an evaluation. International Journal of Science Education, 21 (4) 431-446.

- Naylor S. and Keogh B. (2000) Concept Cartoons in science education. Sandbach: Millgate House Publishers.

- Naylor S., Keogh B. and Dabell J. (2008) Active Assessment: thinking, learning and assessment in mathematics. Sandbach: Millgate House Publishers.

- White R. and Gunstone R. (1992) Probing understanding. London: Falmer.

Useful references to Concept Cartoons

- Downing B. (2005) Developing the nature and the role of quality argument in primary science lessons through the use of concept cartoons. Unpublished PhD thesis, Manchester Metropolitan University.

- Education Extra (1998) Science on the Underground: An evaluation of the concept cartoon project by Education Extra. London: Education Extra.

- Keogh B. (1995) An exploration of the possible value of cartoons as a teaching approach in science. Unpublished MA dissertation, Manchester Metropolitan University.

- Keogh B. and Naylor S. (1993) Learning in science: another way in. Primary Science Review, 26, 22-23.

- Keogh B. and Naylor S. (1997) Making sense of constructivism in the classroom. Science Teacher Education, 20, 12-14.

- Keogh B. and Naylor S. (1998) Teaching and Learning in Science using Concept Cartoons. Primary Science Review, 51, 14-16.

- Keogh B. and Naylor S. (1999) Concept Cartoons, teaching and learning in science: an evaluation. International Journal of Science Education, 21,4,431-446.

References

- Keogh B. & Naylor S. (2000) Teaching and learning in science using Concept Cartoons: why Dennis wants to stay in at playtime. Investigating 16, 3, 10-14.

- Millar L. and Murdoch J. (2002) A penny for your thoughts. Primary Science Review, 72, 26-9.

- Naylor S. and Keogh B. (1999) Science on the Underground: an initial evaluation. Public Understanding of Science, 8, 1-18.

- Naylor S. and Keogh B. (1999) Constructivism in the classroom: Theory into Practice. Journal of Science Teacher Education, 10(2) 93-106.

- Naylor S. & Keogh B. (2002) Concept Cartoons. Teaching thinking, 9, 8-12.

- Naylor S., Keogh B., de Boo M. and Feasey R. (2000) Researching formative assessment: concept cartoons as an auditing strategy. In R.Duit (Ed.) Research in Science Education: Past, Present and Future. Dordrecht: Kluwer.

- Naylor S., Keogh B. and Downing B. (2007) Argumentation and primary science. Research in Science Education, 37, 17-39.

Concept Cartoons and Active Assessment publications

- Dabell J., Keogh B. and Naylor S. (2007) Thinking about maths poster set. Sandbach: Millgate House Publishers.

- Keogh B. and Naylor S. (1997) Starting points for science. Sandbach: Millgate House Publishers.

- Keogh B. and Naylor S. (1997) Thinking about science poster set. Sandbach: Millgate House Publishers.

- Keogh B. and Naylor S. (1999) Thinking about science 2 poster set. Sandbach: Millgate House Publishers.

- Keogh B., Dabell J. and Naylor S. (2008) Active Assessment: thinking, learning and assessment in English. Sandbach: Millgate House Publishers.

- Naylor S. and Keogh B. (2000) Concept Cartoons in science education. Sandbach: Millgate House Publishers.

- Naylor S. Keogh B. and Goldsworthy A. (2004) Active Assessment: thinking, learning and assessment in science. Sandbach: Millgate House Publishers.

- Naylor S., Keogh B. and Dabell J. (2008) Active Assessment: thinking, learning and assessment in mathematics. Sandbach: Millgate House Publishers.